The Nature of Time

Edited by T. GOLD

WITH THE ASSISTANCE OF

D. L. SCHUMACHER

CORNELL UNIVERSITY PRESS

Ithaca, New York

Copyright © 1967 by Cornell University

First published 1967

Library of Congress Catalog Card Number: 67-23761

PRINTED IN THE UNITED STATES OF AMERICA
BY GEORGE BANTA COMPANY, INC.

THE NATURE OF TIME *is the report of a meeting held at Cornell University on the thirtieth and thirty-first of May and the first of June, 1963. The meeting was convened by Professor H. Bondi and Professor T. Gold, and it was to a large extent supported by a contract and grant from the United States Air Force Office of Scientific Research (No. AFOSR AF49 [638]–1527).*

Preface

The scientists who participated in the meeting recorded in this book were chosen not only for their eminence but also for their willingness to discuss a subject that quite clearly is not well understood. By limiting the gathering to twenty-two people, Professor Bondi and I hoped to promote informal discussion among them and to relieve their embarrassment at having to voice opinions about the nature of time.

It is an embarrassment for a scientist who has concerned himself with the basic nature of the physical laws to have to admit that the coordinate system in which the laws are imbedded is itself quite mysterious. Lack of understanding is not the only difficulty; many other areas of physical science are not well understood. But in this case the problem is so fundamental that no thoughtful scientist can claim to have given it no consideration. Most believe that they have gained some basic understanding and are then distressed to find a divergence from the views of their colleagues. Introspective understanding of the flow of time is basic to all our physics, and yet it is not clear how this idea of time is derived or what status it ought to have in the description of the physical world.

The invitation to the participants contained the statement that the subjects we intended to discuss would include the following:

1. Cosmic time and the notion of large-scale change; thermodynamic or entropic time in cosmology; advanced and retarded potentials; suitability of the notion of progressing time for the discussion of cosmology and small-scale physics.

2. Irreversible processes in general; entropy in thermodynamics and information theory.

3. Microphysics—irreversibility in quantum physics; theory of measurement; PCT theorem and related matters.

Most of these subjects are in fact included in the conversations as reported here. But the reader must not expect any very systematic treatment or course of instruction. Instead he will find, in addition to a number of prepared papers, a lot of conversation that is sometimes deep, sometimes flippant, and sometimes, I am afraid, incomprehensible.

There were severe doubts whether the proceedings of the conference should be published. The informality of the meeting might make for difficult reading; the absence of an audience allowed the participants a degree of freedom of expression not generally acceptable in scientific writing. The impression that a spoken remark makes on a small group of colleagues can be judged well on the spot—but it may not be at all the same as that which it will make on the reader. Still, at the end of the conference I urged publication, and all but one of the participants were agreeable. I urged publication because it seemed to me that students of the subject should be informed not only of the aspects that are understood and presented here, but also of the profound uncertainties, the basic divergences of opinion that exist in so fundamental a discussion. Most young persons beginning work in a field believe it to be fairly systematic and well understood, and as they learn more are disappointed at the muddled thinking, the ignorance, and the uncertainty among experts. This disillusionment is an essential part of the learning process. It is this that usually gives the student the courage to enter the fray himself. If this report fails to have any other useful results, I am sure it will make amply clear, through the degree of understanding that has been achieved, that the subject is not forbidding.

One participant, hereafter referred to as "Mr. X," was against publication. To him the informality of the conversation had been such an essential part of the conference that he felt our promised privacy was being violated. He would have prepared his remarks quite differently for publication. Really, of course, he was more consistent than the rest of us, who pretended to ignore the tape recorder when it should have looked to us like a large audience listening to our deliberations. Still, Mr. X did not insist on forbidding the publication. His contributions have, however, not had the benefit of his corrections and may be on occasions incorrect through mistakes in transcription. The reader is therefore requested not to quote Mr. X.

I hope that the process of transcribing and editing and the work of the participants in checking their contributions have led to a text that in the main represents what was said. I am sure, though, that some errors and discrepancies will remain, and for these I offer my apologies.

The difficult work of transcribing from the tapes was carried out by Mrs. A. Echandi and the first round of editing by Mr. B. Ulrich. The main tasks of editing, corresponding with the participants, and preparing the final draft were carried out by Mr. D. L. Schumacher. These three have my thanks for what proved to be an arduous task.

But chiefly I must thank the participants, for they made this book through their efforts in coming to the meeting, contributing papers and discussion, correcting transcripts, and above all giving us the benefit of their understanding of many aspects of this vexing subject.

T. GOLD

Cornell University
March 1967

Contents

Participants

P. G. BERGMANN, Department of Physics, University of Syracuse

H. BONDI, Department of Mathematics, King's College, University of London

S. CHANDRASEKHAR, Laboratory for Astrophysics and Space Research, Enrico Fermi Institute for Nuclear Studies, University of Chicago

T. GOLD, Center for Radiophysics and Space Research, Cornell University

A. GRÜNBAUM, Center for Philosophy of Science, University of Pittsburgh

M. HARWIT, Center for Radiophysics and Space Research, Cornell University

J. HOGARTH, Department of Physics, Queen's University, Kingston, Ontario

F. HOYLE, St. John's College, Cambridge University

D. LAYZER, Department of Astronomy, Harvard University

C. MISNER, Department of Physics and Astronomy, University of Maryland

P. MORRISON, Department of Physics, Massachusetts Institute of Technology

J. V. NARLIKAR, King's College, Cambridge University

R. PENROSE, Department of Mathematics, Birkbeck College, University of London

W. RINDLER, Southwest Center for Advanced Studies, Dallas, Texas

I. ROBINSON, Southwest Center for Advanced Studies, Dallas, Texas

L. ROSENFELD, Nordisk Institut for Teoretisk Atomfysik, Copenhagen

E. SALPETER, Department of Physics, Cornell University

L. SCHIFF, Department of Physics, Stanford University

D. L. SCHUMACHER, Center for Radiophysics and Space Research, Cornell University

D. W. SCIAMA, Department of Applied Mathematics and Theoretical Physics, Cambridge University

J. A. WHEELER, Palmer Physical Laboratory, Princeton University

MR. X

THE NATURE OF TIME

Introduction

T. GOLD AND H. BONDI

GOLD

I wish first to welcome my distinguished colleagues; we are very honored that you have all responded to this invitation.

The organization of this meeting is minimal. We wanted to make it a discussion meeting around the table, and we have therefore tried to avoid the distractions that would arise from a larger group and from holding the meeting in a bigger room with a large audience. I had to resist strong pressures in this respect. Many other people wanted to join the meeting, and I am sure that some of them would have made interesting contributions. Nevertheless, the meeting would have become much more formal. I felt that there was a strong case for maintaining a kind of informality such that we can speak our minds and have a free give-and-take in an argument, rather than be forced to make speeches.

The problem that we are here to discuss, the problem of time, is a very strange one. Nearly everyone who works in physics has come to the conclusion that an understanding of the nature of time is basic. Each physicist has developed a point of view about it. There are great divergences in these points of view which have not been well aired; the literature is disappointingly limited in this subject. I think we shall discover that there is no agreement regarding even the most basic matters. It amazes me that a concept like time can have such a profound tradition in the physical sciences in spite of the fact that it is regarded in such widely different ways.

Is the lack of agreement due perhaps to the fact that a sensible outlook has not yet been developed? We seem to derive the notion of a flow of time in the first place from introspection. We then use the introspective notion to classify observations in the physical world. But does

1

physics suggest that the flow of time is the only appropriate or the only possible representation? Perhaps the introspective notion is quite unsuitable. Perhaps it is only a deception of a biological sort which ought to have no place in physics.

Is it really basic to the description of physical processes that time progresses? Or does the set of world lines of all the particles comprise a great pattern which represents the entire physical world without reference to any passage of time or to any idea of flow? Must we think of the laws of physics as operating upon the present to produce the future? Or are the laws of physics to be considered merely as certain relationships that can be recognized in this great pattern? Is everything being pushed along the time coordinate as the chips are pushed by the croupier's rake? Or is it only through the details of the interrelation between events in space-time and the information within the brain, which are part of the great pattern, that biological mechanisms have devised a representation in terms of flowing time? If this is so, then perhaps it is wrong to carry over the concept of time in a description of nature. These are questions which I hope will come to the fore in these discussions, and they seem to me more important and less well understood than such matters as the relationship between the aniso-tropy of time and thermodynamic processes. That is a matter which is now fairly well understood and evidently does not lead to a complete understanding of the major problem.

BONDI

The purpose of my remarks is to raise blood pressures so that the discussion may get going reasonably soon and in a suitably fierce way. I am aided by the fact that Gold has already touched on the first point of what is meant by the direction of time, namely, the sense in which we can relate the subjective experience to the four-dimensional pattern. Only one point seems to me at all clear: it is only the three-plus-one dimensional structure of space-time that gives the possibility of having a distinction in patterns, one within the other. We cannot conceive of any such directionality, whatever it may be, even in matters of thermo-dynamic reversibility, in relation to the space coordinates, without introducing new concepts and new ideas.

If we leave aside discussion of the points where physics either is in fact completely reversible or is what might be called "indistinguishably reversible"—that is to say, where we change other things along with the time-reflection and then arrive at a situation which internally is indistinguishable from the original one—then, to my mind, there are three topics where we come across the significance of the direction of time in physics. One of course is the well-known thermodynamical topic, related to the statistics of things; the second one is the topic of electromagnetic radiation; and the third is cosmology. About the topic of thermodynamics, the view is really determined independently by our assumptions, just as in the electromagnetic case. In this connection we may allude to the classical story in which we are given two photographs of the box of gas. In one of the photographs the gas is all over the box, and in the other it is in one half of the box. We are told that these are successive photographs and that the gas was not disturbed between the times the two photographs were taken. We are not told which was the first photograph and we are asked to arrange the photographs in time. Most people will say that the photograph showing all the gas on one side is the first one. But when this statement is analyzed, it is seen to be unsound. If we put all the gas on one side of a membrane, by means of a pump, and then remove the membrane, letting the gas go across, a subsequent photograph will show a correlation between position and velocity of the gas molecules. Starting from this subsequent arrangement of the gas molecules, but with their velocities reversed, the gas will after some time be in half of the box. Accordingly, what we judge in ordering the photographs in time is *only* the technical competence of the experimenter. We usually deny the experimenter the competence to put the gas molecules into random position and to give them velocities such that after some time they will be on one side. This is a typical case which shows how we are conditioned to make certain sets of assumptions and how awkward it is to wriggle out of them. And these assumptions very often are what effectively determines our views on this question.

When we come to the question of electromagnetic radiation, retarded potentials, advanced potentials, and the like, the situation is not very different in that our attitude is very largely based on a prejudgment. If we know that there is a retarded potential, we call the source an "emitter." When we know there is an advanced potential, we call it an "absorber." If we see both, we call it a "scatterer." A judgment of likelihood essentially determines these choices. If in order to get a particular picture we have to assume that closely correlated waves come from all directions from infinity, then we regard this situation as very unlikely. However, if we picture closely correlated waves going out to infinity, then we are not similarly prejudiced against it. But it is an assumption about what goes on at infinity that prejudges the issue.

The third relevant topic is the cosmological one related to the expansion of the universe. If it is agreed that the expansion of the universe has a lot to do with the problem of time, a conclusion which I regard to be virtually inescapable because this process leads to the dark night sky, to the disequilibrium between matter and radiation, and to the fact that radiated energy is effectively lost, then we accept a very close connection between cosmology and the basic structure of our physics. This seems to be very worrisome for any cosmological model in which the universe contracts at some stage. It seems to me that, quite apart from the problem of what an observer would see due to such a contraction, we should have to answer, far more carefully than we have so far, the questions about the thermodynamics in the contracting universe. Only when this investigation has been made would I be willing to regard any conception of a contracting universe as a serious physical model, and not as merely a geometrical arrangement, perhaps quite instructive in some respects, but an arrangement which leaves out an essential aspect of physics.

If, however, we wish to work out in detail how the expansion of the universe is linked with the direction of time, then the very great conceptual difficulty arises that our physics is derived in the presence of the universe. We are forced to make some arbitrary assumptions about which processes are truly elementary and "independent," as it were, of the universe, then combine such processes to account for the thing we see, the expanding universe, and thus explain the things which are not elementary but due to long-range interactions. A very grave question about any such world model which links the depths of the expanding universe with our local system is that we have made a completely arbitrary decision as to which parts of physics are purely elementary and which are not. I think that the most we can hope for is a self-consistent scheme.

MORRISON

I think you mentioned correctly the three areas where we have the question of the anisotropy. I thought, however, that there was an assumption concealed within the adverb "only." You said the ordering of the photos was "only a judgment of our technical competence." I think that the only important thing is the technical competence of the experimenter.

BONDI

The question of anisotropy has nothing to do with our rules for the intrinsic behavior of the gas. The ordering is a judgment of likely or unlikely initial conditions. This is the whole question.

GOLD

Then if we treat a system composed of sufficiently few particles, we cannot order the photographs in time. Not only is this ordering impossible, but it is meaningless to consider such a system as imbedded in a flowing time.

MORRISON

Yes, insofar as it is a subsystem which is completely decoupled from systems which are complex. This situation is not so easy to find, either.

X

Why is it meaningless to consider this subsystem in a flowing time? Is it not still in a flowing time even if the time direction is not known?

BONDI

The time coordinate is in any case on the same footing as the space coordinate. It is a continuously varying one with a certain continuity.

MORRISON

But the anisotropy is only one of the many properties of time. Why should we restrict the problem to anisotropy? Is time exactly the same as space or is it different from space? This question is something which we usually pay little attention to; the field-theory people should have a lot to say about it.

BONDI

The point about the distinction between space and time coordinates is that if we try to single out one space direction from the others, calling it "positive," then there are permissible rotations which change it. But if we call a direction of time "positive," then no proper Lorentz transformations can change it.

X

Aside from the property of continuity, and from the time-reversal problem, there is also the question of homogeneity. I realize that this problem is connected with the cosmological question. If we deny the "perfect cosmological principle," then time is inhomogeneous. Either there is invariance under a translation along the time axis, or else translation is not an invariant property and there is an absolute origin.

ROBINSON

One plane wave I happen to know has the agreeable property that there is an absolute. There is one particular wave front which we might describe as the origin, and all the other wave fronts are indistinguishable from each other. We do get from one point to another along the spatial axis, but not by translation, and there is no way of distinguishing one point from another.

BERGMANN

Yes. In that case certainly translation is not an invariant operation.

I. Absorber Theory of Radiation[1]

J. HOGARTH

My discussion is concerned with time-symmetrical electrodynamics and is based essentially upon the question expressed by

$$\sum_{j \neq i} \tfrac{1}{2} \{ F_{\text{ret}}^{(j)} + F_{\text{adv}}^{(j)} \} \overset{?}{=} \sum_{j \neq i} F_{\text{ret}}^{(j)} + \hat{F}^{(i)}. \tag{1}$$

If we think of the $F^{(j)}$ as the electromagnetic field associated with the particle which has been labeled "j," and if we sum over the fields of all particles except that of the particle "i" itself with which we are concerned, then the sum $\sum_{j \neq i} F_{\text{ret}}^{(j)}$ represents the retarded force acting on the particle "i." In addition we then have another quantity $\hat{F}^{(i)}$, which is the force of radiative damping. In Dirac's description of this term,

$$\hat{F}^{(i)} = \tfrac{1}{2} (F_{\text{ret}}^{(i)} - F_{\text{adv}}^{(i)}). \tag{2}$$

It is rather cumbersome to discuss this problem in terms of fields; we really should be discussing it in terms of direct interparticle action. This discussion of course is a continuation of the work of Wheeler and Feynman, who did their work in terms of direct interparticle actions in Minkowski space. I have tried to pursue the problem in the case of conformally flat spaces.

For my purposes, $F_{\text{ret}}^{(j)}$ means that we have a particle labeled "j" with some motion. We solve Maxwell's equations for that particle as the only inhomogeneity in the field, and with the boundary condition that we allow only outgoing waves from the particle. We define similarly $F_{\text{adv}}^{(j)}$, and so forth. Now, if we say that Maxwell's equations in themselves do not reveal any asymmetry with respect to time, then this particular solution, half the sum of retarded and advanced fields, is the only one which does not exhibit an arrow of time. So the questions I pose are whether we can add up as the force acting on the particle

7

"*i*" the sum of all these things for all the other particles, and whether there will be conditions under which the right and left sides of the equation (1) will be equal, or approximately equal.

We are really trying to do two things, to set forth a consistent time-symmetrical electrodynamics and to find the source, so to speak, of the force of radiation damping. Suppose we just assume that there is an electrodynamic arrow of time and that we do not require a particular form of the solution of Maxwell's equation. Any solution which is a normalized linear combination of F_{ret} and F_{adv} is of course a solution, so we could write more generally what we might want to look for as

$$\sum_{j \neq i} (aF_{\text{ret}}^{(j)} + (1 - a)F_{\text{adv}}^{(j)}) \overset{?}{=} \sum_{j \neq i} F_{\text{ret}}^{(j)} + \hat{F}^{(i)}.$$

By slight rearrangement, we have

$$2(a - 1) \sum_{j \neq i} \hat{F}^{(j)} - \hat{F}^{(i)} \overset{?}{=} 0.$$

If we have N particles, then we have N linear simultaneous equations in the $\hat{F}$'s, one for each particle. There will actually be $6N$, because F represents a tensor having six independent components, but we can think of this number as N. We may ask under what conditions we have a solution. The determinant of the coefficient must of course vanish, giving rise to an Nth degree polynomial in a, and all these solutions are equal except one. We find that $N - 1$ of the solutions of a are $\frac{1}{2}$. When we put the value $\frac{1}{2}$ into this matrix, the matrix is of rank 1, so this implies only one condition on the $\hat{F}$'s. That condition is $\sum_{j \neq i} \hat{F}^{(j)} = 0$, which is the condition found by Wheeler and Feynman.

The other value that a can have is something like $1/(N-1)$. There are $N - 1$ conditions which say that all the $\hat{F}$'s are equal everywhere. Since these are field quantities, all particles must be superimposed. This condition is of course unphysical, so if we want equation (1) to hold and to explain the source of radiation damping in terms of fields associated with particles, the only choice is $a = \frac{1}{2}$.

We are trying to see if there is a cosmology in which (1) is true for every particle. Establishing the equality of (1) everywhere does not in itself provide an electrodynamic arrow of time. If we change the order of time, we get the same expression. Only if we can physically dissociate F_{adv} and F_{ret} can we talk about an electrodynamic arrow of time.

Now, of course, this brings us into all sorts of philosophical discussions about the observer, and I intend to surmount these simply by ignoring them. We assume that the right-hand side characterizes classical electrodynamics, and that it has an electrodynamic arrow of time in the sense that we can talk about $\sum_{j \neq i} F_{\text{ret}}{}^{(j)}$ and $\hat{F}^{(i)}$ separately for a particular particle. My picture of this situation involves doing a hypothetical experiment with the same universe in two different states. In one state, the particle "i" exists over an arbitrary region of space-time; in the other, it does not exist there. We ask what is the field in the region of that bit of world line if the particle is not there. Then we put the particle there with some motion that we prescribe. We ask what additional fields now arise in the region of the particle because of it, not fields due to the particle itself, but those due to the existence of the particle. This new field we call the field of radiation damping as described by Dirac in equation (2). So $\sum_{j \neq i} F_{\text{ret}}{}^{(j)}$, although it has an effect on the detailed motion of the particle, is to be independent of the detailed motion, whereas $\hat{F}^{(i)}$ is to be completely determined by the motion.

With this in mind, we picture our universe as having essentially no fields in the region near the particle. If fields were present, we could just add them in. After we put the particle in, it has an associated physical field defined by half its retarded fields plus half its advanced fields as we defined them. Those fields stimulate the universe within this particle's null cone, perhaps in both directions, and the universe is jiggled because of this particle and its motion. We assume spherical symmetry; this is to say that the fields which have sources elsewhere have the same kind of spherical symmetry as the field of the particle we are looking at. The part of the universe in the future null cone will have advanced fields which have some value on this particle's null cone. The part of the universe in the past will have retarded fields. The advanced fields whose sources are in the future part we call Φ, and the retarded fields whose sources are in the past part we call Π. The two key equations are

$$\Phi = f(\hat{F} + \Pi)$$

and

$$\Pi = p(-\hat{F} + \Phi).$$

Of course, the field Π arises from motion in the past which is caused by the fields which go into the past absorber, namely Φ, and by the advanced part, $\frac{1}{2}F_{adv}^{(i)}$, of the original field, $\frac{1}{2}(F_{ret}^{(i)} + F_{adv}^{(i)})$, of the particle. This total field, other than the one that originates in the past absorber, is called the "stimulus" of the past absorber, and there is a similar "stimulus" for the future. So $-\hat{F} + \Phi$ is the stimulus of the past absorber, and $\hat{F} + \Pi$ is the stimulus for the future absorber. Now the f and the p are just mappings that map Φ into Π.

We assume that Φ and Π, at least in the neighborhood of a source particle, are complex numbers if the field components themselves are described by complex exponential functions. These equations have interesting solutions because if, for example, only one of these maps is unity, then one of the solutions is independent of what the other solution is. That is the key point in my argument. If, for example, what I call the future absorber is "ideal," that is, if $f = 1$, then $\Phi = \hat{F}$ and $\Pi = 0$ regardless of what p is unless $p = 1$. If $p = 1$, and $f \neq 1$, then $\Phi = 0$, and $\Pi = -\hat{F}$. If $f = p \neq 1$, that is, if the future and past absorbers have the same properties, then

$$\Phi = -\Pi = \frac{f\hat{F}}{1 + f},$$

and the response of both absorbers taken together is zero. If $f = p = 1$, we get the indeterminate situation; the two equations are then the same equation, and we have no unique solution. This, I claim, is the situation which allows the Wheeler-Feynman theory for static space to be consistent both ways.

The question now is whether, if we reduce the question expressed by equation (1) to the study of the f and p equations, we can find the f and p for a particular cosmology. If we know the geometry of the universe, then we can check what these things are independently of each other. The procedure is as follows. Suppose, for example, that we have a particular cosmological model with a particular spherically symmetric density of matter. We take a particle, give it an arbitrary motion, and calculate the full retarded field of that particle, $F_{ret}^{(i)}$. This is just a mathematical exercise. Then we look for a solution of Maxwell's inhomogeneous field equations in the future absorber with boundary conditions in the neighborhood of the test particle's null cone. This is a solvable problem in principle, although it is difficult in practice. If we then have the field everywhere, we can determine from the Lorentz equations of motion what the motions of the particles are on the null cone. Knowing these motions we can calculate their half-advanced sum at the initial point, which, according to this principle, is the reaction of the future absorber. We can show that it is a necessary and sufficient condition for $f = 1$ that the sum of the advanced field at that point is just $\frac{1}{2}\hat{F}^{(i)}$.

This involves the one difficult problem of finding solutions of Maxwell's inhomogeneous equations in the cosmological space. I used the classical solution on a little piece of locally flat space-time, then found out what the wave is doing there and transformed this to a global set of coordinates and got the solution everywhere. This method, of course, is a very imprecise sort of thing. For example, among the assumptions were the approximations that the partial derivative of the frequency of the wave with respect to the radial coordinate is vanishingly small, that the partial derivative of the change of refractive index is vanishingly small, and so forth. In order to get a sensible solution for any universe, we must have a converging integral, and this requires a damping of the wave along the null cone at a faster rate than the normal $1/r$ dependence. This damping would be provided through a complex refractive index with appropriate sign. Of course the sign we use is really the arrow of time itself in a sense, although this damping, this complex or imaginary part of the refracting index, is anyway merely engineering. Nevertheless, there is a crucial point about the sign that we give to this imaginary part. In my paper I chose different signs for future and past so that both regions give convergent results. This amounts to saying that the observed damping is a function of radius, and not of any presupposed arrow of time. For example, suppose we have a time-symmetrical electrodynamics in the case of a sphere, and we produce a disturbance inside this sphere. This assumption really amounts to the question: Can something go on inside while nothing happens outside as a result? If that is possible, then we can break the effect of the perfect absorber down into steps, so that the attenuation is a function of r, independent of which way it is in time. I used this sort of argument for myself in order to justify the use of this sign.

There is one other possible interpretation of how the wave can be attenuated as it progresses through the medium in either sense of time from the source of the disturbance. The matter in this region is not smooth. We have taken it to be smooth, but of course in an actual universe there are discontinuities in the density. Each discontinuity in the density scatters some of the energy in order to match up the boundary conditions across this discontinuity. There are ways in which that scattered energy can get back to the same null cone. It can be scattered again, for example. But in phase it will be incoherent with the unscattered wave which is progressing along the cone. So in terms of the coherent wave, there could be an attenuation along the null cone which is a function of r rather than of t because of the number of discontinuities that are crossed.

By change of variable from the radial coordinate in the conformally flat metric to a new variable which is a function of this coordinate, the variables show a phase invariance. As the wave progresses through matter there is a sine wave along the light cone. If it travels through empty space, then the wave is all in the same phase. We can use a parameter which is proportional to the number of phase changes along the cone, so that the appropriate equation is just the one that Wheeler and Feynman found when using flat space and the variable r. Because of this result, the troublesome integral needed to be only slightly different to get some convergence. So first we should consider what difference the approximation makes for this integrand. The integrand might even converge without the nasty business of resistance damping. For this reason a student and I tried to find exact solutions of Maxwell's equations in conformally flat spaces with different distributions of, say, charge without free electrons. We were able to find a particular gauge that gave a potential for which the variables r and t were separable: $\phi^\mu = R(t)\xi(r)$. The part of the function in r turned out to be the same as it is in flat space, so it can be integrated. It is just a complex exponential or trigonometric function. The t function satisfies

$$f'' + (\omega^2 + \lambda e^{(2-k)\psi})f = 0.$$

Here, the ω is a separation constant; the λ is proportional to the density N of electrons; the $e^{\text{const}\cdot\psi}$ is the conformal factor in the metric; $k=0$ for creation of matter such that the density is constant, and $k=3$ for no creation. So this is the differential equation satisfied by the time part of the potential of the field we are looking at. This is an exact equation; the only approximations are that the velocities are small and essentially comoving. This equation, of course, gives rise to Bessel functions. But of course we can see that if $e^{(2-k)\psi}$ is slowly changing, we can have approximate trigonometric solutions for any value of t.

Another intriguing thing about t is that if you take $k=2$, there is some creation, but it is not fast enough to give steady-state conditions. We then get trigonometric solutions in terms of t, which is not the proper time, but the coordinate time. In terms of t, exactly, there is no problem at all. One small way in which we can try to patch up a solution is to break the space-time into slabs for different times. Put $k=2$ in all the slabs, but have the density change from one slab to the next so that the average density is changing in the required way. This is not the normal type of spacelike boundary that is encountered in electromagnetic equations. In effect, there is a certain medium for which the equations can be solved exactly, and then the medium is suddenly changed. The frequency changes in this case, whereas the wavelength remains fixed. By this method we can do a sort of ray-tracing of the field due to the particle. I got the same result as I did by taking the local Cartesian solution and then changing the coordinates to get the solution in terms of the global coordinates.

If we define the arrow of time as that direction in the cosmological model for which the radiation damping is of the right sign, then we can relate that arrow of time to the large-scale motion of the universe. In this particular calculation, the steady-state model gave an expanding universe and the Einstein–de Sitter model gave a contracting universe.

X

In the relation of electrodynamical time to cosmological time, we have to be precise about what problem we are trying to solve. There are three arrows, maybe more. One might be called, just for simplicity, a "thermodynamic arrow," or the "accidents of life arrow." Its origin is unknown. Then there is the "retarded or advanced arrow" which we may call the "radiation arrow." There is also the "cosmological arrow" which has to do with whether the nebulae are getting closer or farther apart. For instance, suppose we have in a single picture a tank of water with a lot of blue water on one side and white water on the other, an antenna with a shaking charge, and the distant nebulae. Take another picture showing the water mixed up, and the question arises: Is the radiation further away from the antenna and are the nebulae getting further apart? Or is the radiation of the antenna further away, say, but the nebulae closer in? Let us take one of the arrows to define the time. We call the direction of thermodynamics the positive direction of time. The question then is which way the radiation goes and which way the cosmology goes. Now the discussion that we heard just now seems to concern itself with the connection of radiation to cosmology, and this seems to disregard the real, direct, and important connection which exists between radiation and thermodynamics. I think we ought to discuss that aspect of the problem first, because the question of whether the cosmology determines the thermodynamics is different from the one of whether cosmology determines thermodynamics through the radiation. This kind of arrow is at least an important one, and was not discussed in this treatment. It was considered to be "merely engineering."

Consider the case of the static universe. I think that no matter what model we make of an expanding universe which has a special static case, this treatment has to give the correct answer. We can make rules in several ways about the fields that are produced by charges. We could make up a theory in which the fields are all retarded and in which there is radiation resistance, and nothing else; so

$$F = \sum_{j \neq i} F_{\text{ret}}{}^{(j)} + \hat{F}^{(i)}{}_{\text{rad. damping}}. \tag{3}$$

Or we can make up a theory such that from every charge there is a half-retarded and a half-advanced solution,

$$F = \sum_{j \neq i} \tfrac{1}{2} \{ F_{\text{ret}}{}^{(j)} + F_{\text{adv}}{}^{(j)} \}. \tag{4}$$

Or we can make up a theory such that there is nothing but advanced solutions and negative radiation resistance,

$$F = \sum_{j \neq i} F_{\text{adv}}{}^{(j)} + \hat{F}^{(i)}{}_{\text{neg. rad. damping}}, \tag{5}$$

and so on. However, all these solutions agree with Maxwell's equations; we all agree to that. Therefore when we fix upon one of these methods to make the calculation, the difference between our answer and somebody else's answer can always be rationalized in the following way: "We insist on using our method, but we admit the possibility that there are some free waves, solutions of Maxwell's equations coming from empty space, that have no obvious source." Let us fix on one view: all calculations, all analysis and all thinking are to be made in terms of retarded waves and radiation resistance (the ordinary way of looking at the problem), but the theory behind it might be (4), for example. Suppose that the right law for producing fields for a set of many charges is in fact (4), but that we insist of thinking in terms of (3). Then we have to add on to our world the homogeneous field solution of the empty-space equations, because these equations do not give the right answer which we get by using the other rules.

The solution which we add is not given by the action principle. It is a solution of Maxwell's equation without sources, and this solution is different depending on what the rules of the calculation are. If we take a specific example where the symmetric theory is the starting point, this external false field that seems to come from nowhere is actually a measure of the fact that we are doing the problem incorrectly when we think this way. Clearly the thing that is wrong, from the point of view of the retarded-wave theory, must be the presence of a field that has no apparent source.

In the symmetric theory which comes from the action principle of Wheeler-Feynman, the fields satisfy Maxwell's equations with the source being the motion of the particle; we will worry about the motions of the particles later. The question concerns what apparent fields are produced, and they are given by (4). We use this solution for the field without adding anything to it. We can of course solve the problem for the same sources using (3). This way we do not get the same solution for the field; the fields differ, but they differ by a solution of the homogeneous equations. Therefore, if someone insists on using the symmetric theory, we can figure out what he is doing and understand everything that should happen in his situation by using only retarded waves, provided we are willing to add an extra field.

Now the question concerns the rule for the field. From the field behavior at each individual charge, we see that the solution (4) has a special property which can be characterized as follows. There is a wave which comes in and goes out such that the incoming wave, if allowed to go through as if there were no charge, will exactly cancel the outgoing wave. The incoming wave, considered as a homogeneous solution without any sources, keeps right on going; it changes sign, and it becomes a homogeneous solution advanced minus retarded. This is true for each charge and for the sum. Therefore the boundary condition which the retarded-wave theory forms is this: "We are allowing an external field which is coming in from the past, and which is so cleverly designed that when a complete motion is worked out, the outgoing wave is the same, except for sign, as the incoming wave would have been if it went right through." We assume always that the charges move only for a limited length of time. We have only to determine F_H to satisfy the consistency requirement in order to solve this problem in the retarded-wave theory. This method is a very convenient way to understand, at least in the case of flat spaces, what the conclusions of this theory are.

Let us consider the kind of conclusions that we obtain by this kind of argument. As a first example, consider a single charge that oscillates after being hit by a hammer. We use the retarded-wave theory plus the boundary conditions. We should get a retarded wave, but that is no good now, because of the rule that there must be an incoming wave which exactly cancels the outgoing one if it keeps going. This result is wrong, because no incoming wave is an outgoing wave. So we must add a homogeneous solution, and after a bit of trial and error, we discover that we can add $\frac{1}{2}F_{adv}$ as an incoming wave which, if it went through without the matter, would come out as $-\frac{1}{2}F_{ret}$. The actual solution then has the property that the outgoing wave is $\frac{1}{2}F_{ret}$. This result is consistent with saying that the incoming wave should have been $\frac{1}{2}F_{adv}$. So we solved the problem by a sort of trial and error, although we already knew the answer. We notice that the radiation resistance on the charge is offset by the action of the external field, so there is no radiation resistance apparent to the person who is trying to shake the charge.

For the next problem we take the geometrical arrangement shown in Figure I-1. This is just complicated enough to illustrate everything at once. The figure represents a three-dimensional sphere with three holes; a charge is at the center. Now, there are two sets of equations for discussing a system of matter in interaction with radiation. One is the law of fields that are produced, that is, (3) or its equivalent; the other is the response of the matter to the field. That is another set of equations, Newton's laws and so on.

Now, there comes a very important question about the thermodynamics. We assume that after an electron is kicked by a field, it loses its organized energy as it plows through the other atoms, banging against them and so forth. We assume that the thermodynamics of these pieces of material is directed in a certain way. In other words, we assume that the charges slow down because of thermodynamics, not because of radiation resistance. The resistance is perhaps partially radiation resistance; we have to figure out how much, but there is always a place where some mechanical resistance is assumed in order to connect the charge to something else. We therefore have put in an arbitrary one-sidedness by making the matter "absorbing" in the ordinary sense that it damps when you try to shake it. We have to know what kind of matter we are

FIGURE I-1

dealing with. Our matter has time running forward, so it is already unsymmetric. But we know how such matter works, because we have a lot of experience with physics problems, so we can solve this problem. The asymmetry in this theory comes only from the assumption that the material is thermodynamically "one-sided." This thermodynamic assumption "drives" the whole electrodynamics in a closed system. That is the main point—"in a closed system."

To solve the problem, we start with the crudest solution, $F_{ret}=0$, hoping this will work. We shake the charge, and retarded waves come out that go into the walls of the container. The waves shake the atoms in the walls, and the walls make their natural reaction which damps out the wave. The mechanics is standard; the electricity is standard; the only thing is an external field to be discovered later. The advantage in working this way is that we know the solution. Now we find waves going out through the holes. In Figure I-2 the waves come out through the holes in the future, and where there are no holes, the walls are heated. There may be partial reflections and so on, but let's not worry about them. Now the question is: Did we solve the original problem accord-

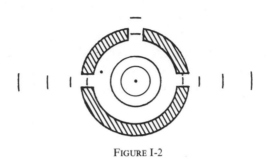

FIGURE I-2

ing to theory (4)? We have to know whether we have an F_H, and the answer is that we must. We did not do it right at first, because at the end of this game there are certain outgoing waves, and we have not satisfied the condition that the incoming waves with a minus sign match the outgoing waves as they would if they went straight through. Therefore in Figure I-3 we use a dotted line to represent the situation in the past. There must be incoming waves in the past to match the outgoing ones, so there must be one wave coming toward one side of the hole that goes all the way through, another coming toward the other side of it, and still another coming toward the wall opposite the hole that does not go all the way through. The last-mentioned wave will hit the back wall before the charge has oscillated, and the outside of the back wall will heat up. This process would not affect the wave heading toward the opposite hole and would not affect the charge in any way.

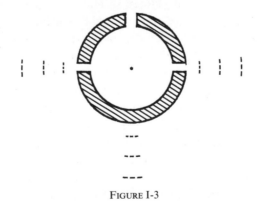

FIGURE I-3

On the other hand, if there are holes on opposite sides of the body, the incoming wave comes through, interacts with the charge, and then passes out the other side. Then we have to make a little self-consistency check. In fact, what happens is that one wave is reduced to half strength in the right solution, and the other is one-half of the advanced piece as in Figure I-4, everything is then consistent.

Now, what happens to the radiation resistance? First, there would be full radiation resistance, but a tuned wave, a wave that is exactly correlated to the way the charge is moving, comes through and acts on the charge. This wave does work on the charge in such a way that the radiation resistance is reduced. The radiation resistance is reduced in propor-

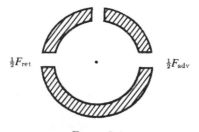

$\frac{1}{2}F_{\text{ret}}$ $\frac{1}{2}F_{\text{adv}}$

FIGURE I-4

tion to the solid angle subtended by the hole. The radiation resistance is reduced insofar as there is light that goes off to infinity and is never absorbed anywhere. That is okay, and, as we would expect, the remaining radiation resistance accounts for the energy which is absorbed in the wall. But as we would not expect, it in addition accounts for the heat that was generated on the back face of the wall opposite the top hole. That outgoing wave is not being compensated by an incoming wave. To summarize, we must add a homogeneous wave, and we always have a solution in which the incoming wave behaves in such a way that if it went through without disturbance it would be equal to the negative of the outgoing wave.

I illustrate this in order to teach how to solve problems easily and in order to describe what happens in different circumstances using the theory of Wheeler and Feynman and using at the same time all the intuition and understanding which we already have from the retarded-wave theory.

Let me make some conclusions with regard to cosmology. Clearly, if the universe is completely closed, this analysis gives the same result as that without any F_H. It has been pointed out by others, in fact by Einstein a long time ago, that in an enclosure with absorbing walls it would not make any difference how we begin. We could even argue that calculation with advanced waves is right. Nevertheless, if we take all the interactions into account, we would get a retarded wave.

The other questions concern open systems. The question which I have not considered concerns a system which is expanding. Suppose simply that in the past the matter was packed tightly so that radiation was absorbed and that in the future the universe becomes rare enough so that it does not absorb at all. We have then a new problem in which the absorbing sphere becomes transparent.

An interesting problem arises in connection with a finite world in which an absorbing sphere has a source at its center. Assume that the sphere was black in the past and is transparent in the future, and that at the present moment we shake the charge. The solution says that the outgoing wave works its way through the walls. There should therefore have been an incoming wave, according to this point of view. But when the incoming wave came, the sphere was black, so there would be no observable effect on the radiation resistance. The two solutions are different if and only if the light can go out to infinity. It is sometimes considered possible that the density of matter decreases fast enough so that as light goes out, it never finds enough absorber. The problem can be done on the basis that the incoming waves which match the outgoing ones are absorbed at great distances. I do not know how to extend this treatment easily to the case of infinite space, nor how to do this problem correctly for a complete universe.

GOLD

But we would have observed this kind of thing incidentally if these effects existed. If the symmetrical theory is in fact right, then we are constrained in an interesting way in our choice of cosmologies.

X

That is quite possible, but we must be careful, because most cosmologies allow the possibility that the absorption in the past is enough to absorb any amount of light that might come in. So there might be some kind of heating at great distances. We must still make a thermodynamic assumption for the cosmos; if we take that assumption out, then we get another kind of problem. This problem is difficult to handle in the case of infinite space, because we do not know where to place the incoming wave. But if we consider the problem as a limit of ever-increasing frequency, then we cannot ever find its effect in the vicinity of the test charge. So there is full radiation resistance even if the universe becomes transparent in the future, but there is an apparent source of heating due to the conservation of energy.

MORRISON

But this heating is as far away in space as it is in time. It might not be observable.

X

The infinity is confusing. Which way do we take the limit? Do we take the case of infinite matter and then try to find a wave, or do we undertake a series of problems about a wave with increasing amounts of matter? We need the solutions in the spherical world in order to understand what to analyze.

GOLD

But it should not be so difficult to say whether a particular cosmological model is right.

X

Yes. The decision about cosmological models should not be too difficult. But the difference between Hogarth's discussion and mine, and the difference, therefore, in the conclusions is that I assumed that matter is thermodynamically one-sided; this assumption does not necessarily make a connection with cosmology. I am not trying to connect the radiation to the cosmological arrow without first making an assumption about the thermodynamic arrow. I am not free to say that the system is symmetrical and that if f is a certain way, then p would have to be a certain way. This situation is not symmetrical in my view.

GOLD

But does not Hogarth's imaginary refractive index determine the thermodynamics already?

X

The sign of the imaginary part of the refractive index in the past was chosen so as to keep the physics symmetrical. The sign of the imaginary part must be wrong in order to make the thermodynamics go right, so in the past the entropy must go one way and in the future it must go the other way.

BONDI

This result means that, in Hogarth's treatment, the advanced wave is enhanced rather than absorbed.

X

Yes. Another argument against this result is that light of a uniform kind would have to be absorbed with different indices. This result would be very problematical, because in the usual view, the field always acts on the particle in the same way.

BONDI

We must discuss the absorption of the waves in terms of the thermo-dynamics and the radiation damping. But what would happen if the matter were superconducting, so that there is pure radiation damping? Would this be a method of getting the direct connection between thermodynamics and radiation?

X

If there is pure radiation with no real damping, then we must use Hogarth's treatment. F_H is no longer necessarily small. There are strong outgoing waves, and the matter is transparent. The situation is very delicate; the light may even create something. I think that there is no particular asymmetry in problems involving the transparent world. We can get different answers, and the answers will not necessarily give a unique direction of time. We need only one grain of sand which is thermodynamically one-sided in order for the time direction to be de-termined.

There may be more than one possible solution for the system having radiation-damping only. In the case of flat space with charges and no resistance, there is an infinite number of self-consistent solutions. With this system alone, there is no absorption, and we can do the problem simply by considering cases of one, two, three charges, and so on.

Suppose that we draw the world lines of two charges as a function of time. If we hit one charge with an external force, there will be an effect on the other one earlier and a corresponding effect on the first one still earlier, and so on. But there is also the possibility that the motion of the first charge was not caused by a kick, but by a bigger motion of the other charge in the past, and a bigger motion of the first, and so on. So there is a solution in which the cause was an infinite kick in the past.

It turns out, however, that the original action principle, from which the differential equation came, can be so stated that this divergent

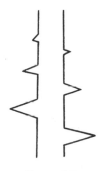

FIGURE I-5

process is not a solution. The limit that was assumed in discussing the divergent case does not exist. We have to find the precise condition placed upon the action. We must calculate the action for a very long, essentially infinite path; when we then take the varied path, we constrain it so that asymptotically it does not vary. Then we take the difference and take the integral to infinity. This result is only defined provided the variation is zero asymptotically. We then suppose that the action is minimum for all such variations. We find that these divergent solutions will not satisfy this condition, because the infinite bumps are fighting against the limit on the variation. The limit does not necessarily exist. This is one way in which we can get rid of divergent solutions. Then maybe the solution is unique. If so, the direction of time would be unique.

Bondi

Is it possible to hit the charge in that case? Is not the solution necessarily trivial?

X

There are only two charges. We can hit one of them with a non-charged object. We can imagine that there is a guy standing there hitting one of the charges. Of course, if there is no external force, this solution just represents some motion of the charges around each other.

BONDI

The trouble is that some formulations do not allow the "guy"; I do not like such formulations.

X

But if there is no guy, we can set up a problem in which the two charges pass each other close by. At the moment they go past each other and accelerate, they must react back on each other. I have not worked out any "unguyed" theories.

HOGARTH

I do not disagree with anything X has said. In our scheme TH↔RAD↔COS, I was working with the connection between RAD and COS. The thermodynamics, in principle, was not supposed to enter into my discussion. I think that X's criticism is that I need to make certain integrals convergent and that I picked up a little piece of thermodynamics and included it for convenience. My next paper will discuss this in more detail. If we make the assumption that the arrow of time in thermodynamics is determined by the arrow of time in radiation, then we can try consistency tests. We can see that this assumption works for one direction of time but not for the other.

The type of attenuation that was necessary to make these integrals converge was not critical, and there are possibly other ways to make these integrals converge rather than using thermodynamical arguments. If the integrals converge, then the arrow from COS to RAD is completely self-consistent without introducing thermodynamics.

II. Time-Symmetrical Electrodynamics and Cosmology[1]

F. Hoyle and J. V. Narlikar

There are two problems in connection with the scheme TH↔RAD↔ COS. First, why is there any arrow at all, and second, why do these three arrows seem to be consistent with each other? We shall consider the second problem to begin with. One point of view that we put forward is that the thermodynamic arrow follows from the first two arrows, the cosmological arrow and the electromagnetic arrow.

If we observe a thermodynamic system over a finite length of time, we can decide which is the initial condition and which is the final condition of the system. This allows us to find a time arrow according to thermodynamics. What is it that makes the system go only one way from the initial to the final state although the laws of physics themselves are invariant under time reversal? The point of view which we have is that the universe causes this anisotropy and acts as a sort of sink with which the system is constantly in interaction. This property is due mainly to the fact that the universe is expanding. Because the universe is expanding, as we know from Olbers' paradox, there is a predominance of matter over radiation; the density of radiation is very small. This condition is maintained by the steady-state cosmology, since as the universe expands, the high entropic energy in the form of radiation is continually lost because of the red shift, and new entropic energy in the form of matter is continually being created. This maintains the universe in a constant state of a sink. The tendency of the system to fill the sink is guaranteed by the presence of purely retarded interactions.

In the "big-bang" cosmology, the universe must start with a marked degree of thermodynamic disequilibrium and must eventually run down, so it just happens that at present radiation is less important.

We wish to connect the electromagnetic arrow of time with the arrow of time given by the expansion of the universe, and in the rest of this paper we should not bring in any thermodynamic consideration. We consider all the continuously expanding cosmological models. In order to connect the electromagnetic arrow of time with the cosmological arrow of time, we follow considerations similar to those given earlier by Hogarth. In this we have a time-symmetrical electrodynamics given by the Wheeler-Feynman theory of direct interparticle action. Two world lines, 1 and 2, of matter interact along each other's null cones, as in Figure II-1. A point P on the world line of particle 1 inter-

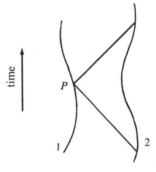

FIGURE II-1

acts with particle 2 through an advanced part above and retarded part below. So this problem is entirely time-symmetrical. We can write down the force on the particle P. We want to see how an arrow of time can emerge from this apparently time-symmetrical description. If we consider each separate particle, we give equal importance to advanced and retarded solutions. Where can the asymmetry come from? The asymmetry would normally come in this case from the asymmetry in the universe. The null cone in the future is different from that in the past. The distribution of the particles, the density, and so forth, in the future is in general different from the distribution in the past, and therefore it is not unlikely that when we perform the summation we may find an asymmetry.

We decided to look for a self-consistent solution. It is important to avoid misunderstanding about the term "self-consistent." When we look for a self-consistent solution with retarded potentials, we are also assuming that F_H, the homogeneous solution that must be added, is zero. We try to find one particular cosmological model in which the F_H is zero. In the Wheeler-Feynman approach, F_H must be zero, since there are no fields without sources.

This restriction makes the problem definite, as can be seen from the following treatment. Suppose we assume that the retarded fields are consistent, and consider a charge "a" with known acceleration $\boldsymbol{u}(t)$. Under the assumption of retarded fields, we know how the field is going to propagate into the future light cone, and we know that the force acting on another particle "b" is given by this retarded field. This force sets the particle in motion, and we consider only that part of the motion of

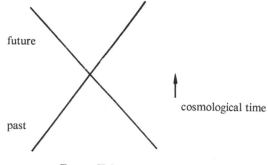

FIGURE II-2

"b" which has been caused by the retarded field of the accelerated charge "a." The principle of direct interparticle action says that, because of the motion of "b," there will be an action back on particle "a." This reaction can be computed, and the summation can be made for all the particles in the universe. For the steady-state model, the assumption of consistent retarded solutions with $F_H = 0$ gives a self-consistent argument. If we consider the corresponding advanced solution, with $F_H = 0$, we do not get a consistent solution for this model. In the case of the Einstein–de Sitter cosmology, the situation is exactly reversed. There is a self-consistent situation for the advanced field and not for the retarded field.

GOLD

Is not "advanced" defined with respect to the motion of the nebulae, so that presumably we would see a contracting universe if we used this solution?

NARLIKAR

Yes. The arrow of time has been fixed beforehand as the one in which the universe expands. Because of the expansion of the universe, there is a difference between the past and the future. An electromagnetic wave which travels in the future is red-shifted and an electromagnetic wave which travels in the past is blue-shifted. This difference may lead to an asymmetry.

To discuss the details of the process, then, we make the assumption of a self-consistent retarded field. As the field propagates into the future, it interacts with other particles, and their motion gives rise to other fields. These new fields modify the original field, with the effect that the medium has a dielectric constant or a refractive index. Some specific assumption must be made about the nature of this refractive index. In order to avoid going into thermodynamics, we decided to stick to pure electrodynamics by assuming that the refractive index arises from the radiative reaction itself. This makes the problem unambiguous. Suppose we must test whether or not F_{ret} is self-consistent. Consider a typical particle and the field nearby it, which is F_{ret}. From F_{ret} we have to subtract the field felt by the test particle, which will be $\frac{1}{2}(F_{ret} + F_{adv})$ according to the action principle. So

$$F_{ret} - \tfrac{1}{2}(F_{ret} + F_{adv}) = \tfrac{1}{2}(F_{ret} - F_{adv})$$

is the field which acts on the particle itself. The F_{ret} is the field acting on the particle, and $\frac{1}{2}(F_{ret} - F_{adv})$ gives the familiar Dirac force of radiative reaction. If, on the other hand, we assume that the fields are everywhere only advanced, then the sign is changed. Therefore we can can give a definite sign for the force of radiative reaction. This follows only from electrodynamic considerations. We can write down the dielectric constant in the form

$$\varepsilon = 1 - \frac{4\pi Ne^2}{m\omega^2}\begin{pmatrix} 1 + O(\omega) \\ 1 + O\left(\dfrac{1}{\omega}\right) \end{pmatrix}.$$

These are limiting values for high and low wavelengths. When we take the square root of this quantity, we have to consider the sign of the terms, and this requires that we know the sign of the radiative reaction. A difference between the past and the future appears because ω is different in past and future. As the electromagnetic wave goes into the future, ω becomes small; as the wave goes into the past, ω becomes large. The variety provided by the different cosmologies is due to the fact that N, the number density of charged particles per unit proper volume, can be different for different cosmologies. For instance, in the steady-state cosmology, N is constant in past and future, and ω of course decreases due to the red shift in the future. Therefore as ω tends to zero, the dielectric constant, ε, is less than zero. If ω tends to infinity, the limit of ε is one. This means that in the case of the steady-state universe, we may specify the cosmological arrow by considering the future light cone of a particular particle. The arrow depends on the "ionosphere" in the future; the past is essentially transparent.

On the other hand, consider the Einstein–de Sitter cosmology, using the same formula. In this case, N is proportional to ω^3. This follows

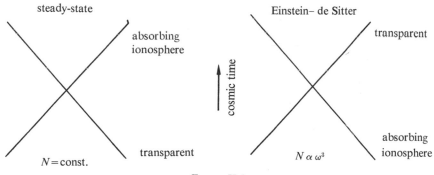

FIGURE II-3

from the fact that matter is conserved, and as the universe expands, the proper density decreases. In the past we get involved with the ionosphere, and the future is transparent. In this result we immediately see the difference between the predictions of the steady-state and Einstein–de Sitter cosmologies. We assume a self-consistent solution with $F_H = 0$ throughout.

WHEELER

How does the expansion rate come into this treatment? Suppose that the expansion rate eventually diminishes to zero. Then surely some dimensionless factor must enter in order to give a transformation over to the usual situation.

BONDI

I think that this is perhaps the most valuable part of Hogarth's analysis. Solving the equations shows how exceedingly critical these parameters are. As long as one side still acts as an absorber, it does not matter what the other side does, unless it is a perfect absorber. The situation becomes exceedingly critical if the past and future absorbers begin to absorb nearly equally. Here the analysis breaks down.

I have wondered what life would be like if the universe were a lot more opaque than it is. We would not be able to see things, and of course there is a case in which all observers would be within adiabatic enclosures, and nothing could happen at all.

MORRISON

I am worried about that. For the refractive index formula, it is assumed in this treatment that there are no inelastic processes. N refers to a number of charged particles, and the system remains neutral overall. But treating the charged particles separately affects the dispersion relations. Do you consider only the electrons or do you actually consider both electrons and protons?

NARLIKAR

Our case is that of one particle only.

MORRISON

There surely is some difficulty in that, because the other particles are there for scattering.

X

Does matter really become transparent at high frequencies? The photons may make pairs, so the medium may get dirtied. Although the atmosphere is transparent for visible light, gamma rays get absorbed.

GOLD

It makes a difference what frequency range we start with. From the radiation-damping idea alone, it is all very well to say that the blue shift is on one side of the light cone vertex and the red shift on the other for electromagnetic radiation in general. If we start with very hard gamma rays, however, we cannot allow any blue shift, because then the gamma rays are easily absorbed, but we can allow a lot of red shift.

It seems that we could even construct a theory in which the interaction of gamma rays is considered, but where ordinary light is forgotten. The direction of the future might even depend on the choice of frequencies, relative to the transparency of the ionosphere. Why do we fix attention on one part of the spectrum?

HOYLE

This choice would not affect the search for the consistent retarded solution, because here we are concerned only with the direction of the future in the case where the frequencies tend to zero. But this does of course raise the question as to what happens on the past half of the light cone.

BONDI

Of course this analysis does not work if the frequency is greater than a certain value. But in my view, it is quite all right to consider the spectrum as a whole, although we must admit that at most frequencies there is absorption before the light plays any part in the analysis. The rest of the frequencies then encounter absorbers which are transparent on one side of the light cone and "ionospheric" on the other.

X

The cross section for absorption of high-frequency gamma rays by atoms approaches a constant. If we have a constant cross section for absorption, and if all the matter of the contracting universe is coming in toward us, as if the thermodynamics goes in the usual way, but the solution of the universe is changed, then I do not understand how the matter can look transparent. By the time a photon reaches a distant nebula, it has become a gamma ray. Does not this imply infinite absorption of such high-frequency gamma rays as they go through the nebulae even if the cross section for the interaction is finite? I am trying to show that everything is still consistent in the case of a contracting universe. The future absorber is also opaque. I do not like making the cross section go down as the frequency goes up.

When there is a binding, then there is an absorption line at that binding energy. The special case of zero-frequency radiation could therefore give trouble. Suppose then that electrons were equipped with a small finite binding, instead of being exactly free. A small binding would enable us to avoid the trouble of waiting for the ultimate absorption at low frequency. Suppose we have an ordinary atom that has some resonance at some finite low frequency. It would then be interesting to integrate the curve of the resonance absorption law from finite frequency, past the bump, down to zero. We can work out the consistent theory of the absorption with that radiation resistance. The only thing that worries me is that by luck all the absorption connected with the index might be at zero frequency. In that case, the frequency could be moved up to a finite value, and then the integral could be calculated to see whether a small number results.

I would not change the assumptions which have been made for this treatment, except to include a binding for charges. I am not arguing about the signs or about thermodynamics. I only suggest changing one little feature before doing the integral. This change is just for technical reasons.

BERGMANN

There is also a physical reason. If the charges have no binding, then there is danger of permanent polarization.

SALPETER

It is said that the contracting case is self-consistent if matter is uniform. Has anyone attempted to see how stellar evolution would go? Has anyone looked in detail at how such a cosmology would work with the condensations we do have?

HOYLE

I think the thermodynamics would also go the other way around in this event. We have to think entirely the other way around. Omit for the moment the possibility that we get into Olbers' paradox, as we probably would. I think that we would actually see the universe contracting.

SALPETER

What worries me is that we would still have a heat engine working as usual, and light would be coming in the usual way. But we would see the distant matter coming at us blue-shifted. There would be an enormous Olbers' paradox.

BONDI

Surely the point is that this problem is difficult enough in the world in which we live! If we try to work through any further consequences in a contracting universe, the situation surpasses the imagination.

SALPETER

I do not quite agree. I think that many of our arguments would become clearer if we considered a cosmological model in which there are different arrows going in different directions. We could really follow out some process and see whether in that case the thermodynamic arrow goes with the cosmology or with the radiation.

NARLIKAR

We now consider the reason for the existence of the time arrow. Here we consider only the case of the steady-state cosmology which has the line element

$$ds^2 = dt^2 - R^2(t)[dr^2 + r^2(d\theta^2 + \sin^2\theta\, d\phi^2)]$$
$$R(t) = e^{Ht}$$
$$H = \text{Hubble's constant.}$$

In the steady-state theory, of course, the density is constant. This result follows from the perfect cosmological principle of Bondi and Gold. The same result can be obtained through Einstein's field equations with an extra term on the right-hand side. More generally, we take a solution of the form

$$R^3 = A(1 + \cosh t);$$
$$\rho = \frac{3H^2}{4\pi G}\frac{\cosh t}{1 + \cosh t},$$

where t is measured in units of $(3H)^{-1}$.

This tends to the steady-state solution as t tends to $\pm\infty$, and, as you see, is time-symmetrical. We have chosen the constant of integration so that the origin is at $t=0$. For $t<0$ there is contraction and continuous annihilation of matter, and for $t>0$ there is expansion and continuous creation. As $t \to -\infty$, the solution tends to the steady state with continuous annihilation of matter; at $t \to +\infty$, it tends to steady state with continuous creation. Since Einstein's field equation is time-symmetrical, any terms that can be introduced are also invariant under time reversal because in any case we find a time-symmetrical solution. If t is changed to $-t$, everything is still seen the same way. Now an interesting question arises. Consider what is seen by an observer picked at random in space-time. If he is at $t = +\infty$, he observes expansion, continuous creation, and retarded potentials. If we take the view that the thermodynamic arrow follows the electromagnetic one, then the observer's own thermodynamic development is compatible with this view. If the observer is at the other end of the time axis, toward $t = -\infty$, he sees a similar situation. The thermodynamic development of the universe in this view would again be in the same direction as that in which the universe is expanding. This direction is obtained by changing the direction of t. This observer also sees matter being created as if the direction of time were reversed.

There is no quantum field theory of the continuous matter creation in the steady-state universe, so we may say for heuristic reasons, but without particular justification, that "matter" is created in the part $t > 0$, and that "antimatter" is created in the part $t < 0$, so there is a matter-antimatter symmetry. The terms are only conventions, of course.

In the region about $t = 0$, observers see a mixture of advanced and retarded fields.

MORRISON

A photon that goes into one direction covers essentially all frequencies from the starting frequency. This seems to involve the sum-rule integral, provided that we include the resonance. The implication probably is that there is a range of frequencies for which it makes no difference whether the photon goes into past or future, as far as the cross section is concerned, and that there is a range of frequencies in which this direction does make a difference. On the other hand, I do not know whether the density alone will be enough to give results which are independent of the dispersion. I suspect that the dispersion results are really not important except in determining whether some frequency is above or below the resonance. We cannot include charges initially to produce scattering, and then avoid putting their interaction into the balance.

HOYLE

We of course have the conviction that most of the atoms are ionized, but I agree that in principle one must include this interaction.

BONDI

There are two points in this connection, surely. One is that in the case of something like the Einstein–de Sitter universe, we must allow for a time variation in the ionization, and the other is that in carrying out a calculation, we must make sure, as Gold said earlier, that no process is temporarily reversed.

GOLD

Let us consider the "zig" and the "zag." The lines are the world lines of particles; the solid line stands for a particle in an excited state and the dotted line represents its de-excited state. The slanted line is a light signal. The "zig" is what we see between world lines of particles in the real world.

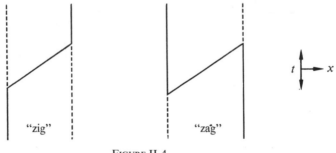

FIGURE II-4

Of course, if we sum the energy during the "zag," we find more than we should have. But the point is surely that *both* the "zig" and the "zag" are completely time-symmetrical.

We can ask why "zigs" occur and "zags" do not. That is one kind of a problem. But the answer to that does *not* tell us where the time asymmetry comes from.

BONDI

The asymmetry is quite clear. To use terms invented earlier, we distinguish between "guyed" charges and "guyless" charges. "Guyed" charges involve information outside the electromagnetic field, such as X's chap who hits the charges; "guyless" charges are the ones that simply follow the field. Then it becomes crystal clear that one of these is hit and the other follows.

GOLD

That is absolute nonsense. We are considering a fundamental process in which an atom spontaneously de-excites itself by emitting a photon which is spontaneously absorbed by another atom. This process is absolutely symmetrical.

X

Absolutely, except for one little thing—the crowd of other atoms!

GOLD

And the absorption of the photon in the crowd of the other atoms is described only by statistics! The light cannot be thought to go in pre-determined fashion from the emitting atom to a select absorbing atom in the crowd. We think rather of the emitter making a puff of light that might involve any atom in the crowd. So there we must worry about statistics.

X

Just put in the other world lines, please. Now, indicate that the other lines sometimes also get excited. Now let's see this reverse!

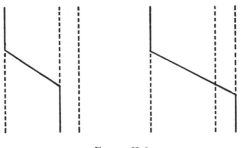

FIGURE II-5

GOLD

That is exactly the point. The asymmetry is only in the statistics.

X

There is another point. Under ordinary circumstances in electrodynamics we have to draw a diagram for each case, starting with the case in which the light is not absorbed anywhere, apart from those for populations of one atom, two atoms, and so on.

GOLD

If the light is not absorbed anywhere, then we have a transparent universe; this is where the cosmology enters the analysis.

SCIAMA

In the case of a static world model the situation is symmetrical, as in Einstein's model of 1917. In an expanding universe, however, the particle world lines which we draw would not be parallel. They diverge because of the expansion. Therefore the time asymmetry arises since there is more energy at emission, say, than at reception.

GOLD

The time asymmetry is in the cosmology and it is in the statistics, but it is not in the electrodynamics. All we need as regards electrodynamics is to know the rule that disallows the "zags." We all agree that this can be done locally anyhow. The mixed "zigs" and "zags" then do not give trouble. The statistics ought to be correlated to the cosmology.

HOYLE

Does not this follow from the assumption of time-symmetrical electrodynamics? The drawing of the "zig" and "zag" implies that there is a cancellation due to emission by the particle. This cancellation is the radiation damping, and this automatically forbids the "zags." This cancellation gives the asymmetry of the damping. It is not asymmetry which tells what parts of the lines are solid; it is the sign of the damping terms. In the time-symmetrical electrodynamics, there is just one allowable one-to-one connection between the sign of the self-consistent solution and the sign of the damping term. This particular connection permits only the "zig."

GOLD

You are saying essentially that I should draw little arrows on the photon lines, so that the incoming ones can be separated from the outgoing ones. Your discussion is not independent of the Wheeler-

Feynman treatment. Any arrow which can be drawn in a way such that the bookkeeping is consistent in the whole diagram does not affect the reversibility of the diagram.

ROSENFELD

The selection of retarded potentials and the use of such figures as these are justified only if the system which we are describing is within a larger absorbing box. Otherwise this argument is not justifiable.

HOYLE

How do we arrive at the "zig" and "zag" diagrams in the first place? Do we not just make the assumption of time-symmetrical electrodynamics from which comes the sign of the radiation damping as a simple matter of consistency? Do we not define the time arrow, the mathematical time, in such a way that a particular field is the retarded one?

X

The sign of damping is determined by the thermodynamic character of the matter in the rest of the universe.

BERGMANN

I believe that we can derive the sign of the radiation-damping term uniquely if we start out with a system which has only the degrees of freedom of a finite number of point charges and of the free Maxwell field. There is no absorber. We write down first the variational principle, which is manifestly Lorentz-covariant. Now we take the total field and dissect it into two parts, one being some sort of Green's functions associated with the particles, the other the remainder, which we may call the "free field," "external field," or whatever we called the F_H. Since we are performing only a mathematical decomposition, we have a free choice, and it does not spoil the physics. It does not matter that the Green's functions are nonsymmetric with respect to the time. We can choose either an asymmetric or a symmetric form. The character of F_H depends, of course, on how we do the splitting; for different choices of Green's functions we will not get the same F_H, no matter what mathematical symmetry is implied. The total set of Lagrange equations for which we want to solve must be equivalent.

Obviously, at one stage of the game we have to do a classical renormalization because the total field at the location of each particle is infinite. This renormalization is straightforward. If we perform it in any manifestly Lorentz-covariant fashion, the sign of the radiation damping comes out uniquely and automatically, depending of course on whether we started by specifying advanced or retarded potentials. If we use the half-advanced and half-retarded potentials, we get zero radiation damping. Since we started with the manifestly Lorentz-covariant variational principle, the Noether theorem automatically gives conservation laws of linear momentum, energy, and angular momentum—all the basic conservation laws. Every type of formalism that we derive will automatically lead to the same conservation laws.

There is one more remark to be made. Since the free field, the F_H, is itself a vacuum solution of the Maxwell equations, no matter how the original formal split was made, it already satisfies the conservation laws. Suppose we had started with the field only, without particles. The field is also Lorentz-covariant and, as we know, also satisfies the conservation laws. If we consider as meaningful only such solutions in which the external field is not excited, then the remainder still has to satisfy conservation laws. This excludes the "zags," provided we have made no mistakes.

X

You have made the mistake of assuming the energy in the field is positive in the "zag" line. If the field energy is negative, the law of energy conservation certainly allows the "zag."

BERGMANN

But I assumed that in fact the field line made no contribution whatever to the energy. The expression for the energy which results from this treatment naturally involves the kinetic energy of the particles, together with an interaction term which is given by the incident field at the location of the particle. The field can be incident from the future or from the past, or from both. There are in any case no electromagnetic degrees of freedom left, since we specifically assumed $F_H = 0$. Since the photon lines are all internal, since they all originate and terminate inside the diagram, they do not contribute to the total energy. Consider this situation (Figure II-6). If we make a determination of the energy at times 1, 2, and 3, then the contributions are as follows: at

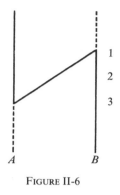

FIGURE II-6

times 1 and 3, the only contributions come from the excited particle; at time 2, the expression for the energy contains a product involving the behavior of the particle itself, its four-velocity, as well as the light cone on which the other particle is located.

X

But then how do you show that this "zag" is impossible?

BERGMANN

By looking in detail at the expressions. We get contributions from particle A and from particle B. The way we calculate, there is no contribution from radiation.

SCHIFF

The argument of the particle energy changes from line A to line B!

BERGMANN

Ah, yes!

X

I still think that the analysis which Bergmann made is very nice. This argument shows further how the thermodynamics is connected to the electrodynamics. If we have been calculating with a Hamiltonian and so forth, then all we have to do is add one more thing to the analysis. What we add is the sort of procedure which is done in statistical mechanics, that of assuming that there is some state which is somehow more ordered than another at a certain time. The resultant system behaves just like those treated by a Boltzmann description; it makes no difference what is assumed about the field. The light is irrelevant, so to speak, since it is "correlated out," and the statistical results do not depend on it. So thermodynamics and light really "lock together" in any situation where they are intimate enough. The only difficulty occurs when the light can be emitted to infinity, or when it escapes. The treatment will always work in the case of a closed box. The thermodynamics and retarded potentials will work together. If we work everything out with advanced potentials, we get the same motions, the same apparent phenomena. We do not necessarily have to assume that the walls of the box are absorbers. The treatment would still work if, say, some of the wall were not.

Bergmann has especially indicated that the field should not be given a status which is in principle different from that of the particles. If we want to understand thermodynamics, we cannot expect to construct a system in which both the light and the particles are to be causally organized. Any kind of organization in particles or fields must be treated *à la* Boltzmann, since it is a Liouville mechanical system. I think that Bergmann has made the connection between the radiation arrow and the thermodynamic arrow. The thermodynamic arrow is the real one, the other is apparent, under Bergmann's assumptions.

III. Cosmological Boundary Conditions for Zero Rest-Mass Fields

R. PENROSE

Suppose we consider solutions to Maxwell's equations in cosmological backgrounds. A question is: When can we call such a solution a purely retarded or purely advanced solution? We are helped in the discussion of these problems by the fact that all isotropic cosmological models are conformally flat, although this property is not essential to the discussion. For, by the conformal invariance of Maxwell's equations, we can, in such cases, reduce the problem to one concerning solutions of Maxwell's equations in flat space. The conformal-invariance property also holds for the Weyl neutrino field and, in an appropriate sense, for gravitation as well. We must be careful in our interpretations, however, because conformal transformations do not, in general, preserve the retarded or advanced nature of a field.

We can write the relevant source-free equations for spins $\frac{1}{2}$, 1, and 2 and for zero mass as follows:

$$\begin{aligned}
\text{neutrino, spin } \tfrac{1}{2}: && \nabla^{A\dot{P}} \nu_A &= 0, \\
\text{photon, spin } 1: && \nabla^{A\dot{P}} \phi_{AB} &= 0, \\
\text{graviton, spin } 2: && \nabla^{A\dot{P}} \gamma_{ABCD} &= 0, \\
\text{where } \nabla^{A\dot{P}} &= \sigma^{\mu A\dot{P}} \nabla_\mu.
\end{aligned}$$

We use two-component spinors throughout. Since the equations must hold in curved space, the differential operators are covariant derivatives. All these spinor quantities are symmetric in their indices. The spinor translation of the Weyl curvature tensor is γ_{ABCD}. If source fields are present, however, then we have terms on the right-hand sides of the equations. These equations have the property that they are conformally invariant. This is the key to the whole procedure. Conformal invariance means, of course, that the equations still hold if we make an "isotropic" space-time "stretch" at each point, which can vary from point to point. That is, using the same coordinates we can change the metric by a factor:

$$\hat{g}_{\mu\nu} = \Omega^2 g_{\mu\nu}; \qquad \hat{\sigma}_\mu{}^{A\dot{B}} = \Omega\sigma_\mu{}^{A\dot{B}},$$

where Ω is a function of position. The various "field equations" are invariant under these conformal transformations provided we take

$$\hat{v}_A = \Omega^{-3/2}v_A, \; \hat{\phi}_{AB} = \Omega^{-2}\phi_{AB}, \; \hat{\gamma}_{ABCD} = \Omega^{-3}\gamma_{ABCD}.$$

By means of such a transformation we can in most cases of interest turn infinity into an ordinary hypersurface, which is a boundary to the transformed space-time. We shall study fields in this transformed space-time instead of in the original physical one. We then have a more "finite" model, and we can, using *local* arguments, examine the behavior of the field at physical infinity. That is, if we examine components of the fields on the *boundary* of the transformed space, we can see what is meant by the radiation field in the *physical* space, and we can therefore define what is meant by purely advanced and purely retarded solutions. Now, the essential point is that in some cosmological models we get a spacelike surface at infinity, in some we get a null surface, and in others we get a timelike surface. Moreover, we may get different types of surface in the past and in the future. It turns out that the kind of surface we get is intimately related to the existence of "visual horizons" (also to the value of the cosmological constant), and to the behavior of radiation.

In all cases, we consider the infinity encountered in *null* directions. This is intimately related to the fact that it is the *zero* rest-mass field equations which are conformally invariant and such fields propagate in null directions. Space-times with null or spacelike surfaces at infinity turn out to be the most important. For Minkowski space, we in fact get a null cone as the future infinity and another null cone as the past infinity.

It must be emphasized that the ordinary null cones in space-time are not altered in the passage to the new conformally transformed space. This is an important feature of conformal invariance—that the null geodesics of the physical space are still null geodesics in the conformally transformed space. However, spacelike and timelike geodesics will not generally remain geodesics.

Now, let us consider, for example, a space with a spacelike boundary at future infinity. An observer's world line then intersects it at "time infinity." This intersection is a perfectly ordinary point on the boundary from the point of view of the transformed space. There will be at that point a past null cone, which divides the space into two regions, containing, respectively, events from which information can reach the observer and events forever hidden from him. Suppose we have, instead, a spacelike boundary surface in the past. Then the past null cones of spatially separated events near enough to this surface will not intersect (that is, such events will be "causally independent" of one another).

In asymptotically flat spaces, both infinites are null as in the case of Minkowski space. In the Einstein–de Sitter model, the future infinity is null. The past infinity is a singular point in the metric, but it so happens that we can do a conformal transformation so that the past infinity is no longer singular, and then it turns out to be spacelike. In the steady-state model, the situation is just the reverse: the future infinity is spacelike and the past infinity is null. This is, perhaps, not really quite fair, as the past infinity is not at infinity from the point of the view of the space-time metric, but it does not seem to make much difference whether infinity is "metrically" at infinity or not. You do not have to do any transformation in the past in the case of the steady-state model.

I must define the notions of "event horizon" and "particle horizon." Consider the totality of events which can be observed by a single observer (that is, consider the part of space-time traced out by the observer's past null cone). An "event horizon" occurs if this part is not the whole space, so that there are events which never become observable by the observer. If all events are ultimately observable by the observer, then there does not exist an event horizon. The event horizon divides the observable from the unobservable for a *given* observer (that is, taking the entire observer's world line as given). There are, of course, world lines of other observers which cross the given observer's event horizon. From the preceding discussion, it follows that *an event horizon exists when future infinity is spacelike* (Figure III-1). On the other hand, if future infinity is null (a null cone), the world lines of all observers (normally) pass through the vertex of this null cone when they reach the boundary. The ultimate null cones of all observers will then all coincide with the future boundary to the universe, so that *there is no event horizon when future infinity is null* (Figure III-2).

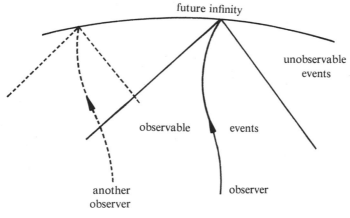

FIGURE III-1

A "particle horizon" exists if, for an observer at an event in space-time, the "substratum particles" in the universe can be divided into two sets, those that he can see and those that he cannot see. This situation occurs when past infinity is spacelike. For, in this case, the starting points of the world lines of the substratum particles are spread out over the whole of past infinity. The past light cone of the observer (normally) intersects only a *subset* of these substratum particles, namely those that he can "see" at any one time. Thus, *a particle horizon exists when past infinity is spacelike* (Figure III-3). A characteristic feature of

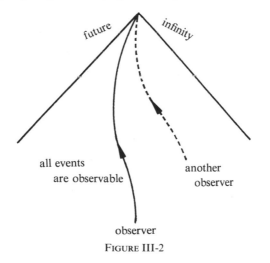

FIGURE III-2

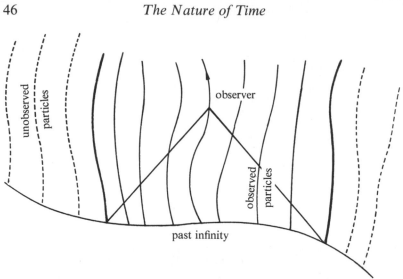

FIGURE III-3

particle horizons is that "waiting" helps; if the observer looks later he will see particles he could not see earlier. If past infinity is a null cone, then all the world lines of the substratum particles will originate at the vertex. The past light cone of any observer will then (normally) intersect *all* these world lines, so that *there is no particle horizon when past infinity is null* (Figure III-4). This is just the time reverse of the situation for the event horizon.

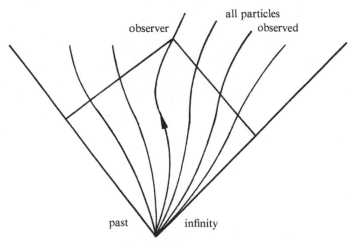

FIGURE III-4

WHEELER

Suppose that the inability of the observer to see certain events is due not to something in the geometry which intervenes between them, but to the fact that the observer crashes into a region of space having infinite curvature and gets killed. Is the concept of horizon valid in this case? I mention this on account of the similar features in the case of the Schwarzschild metric.

PENROSE

These horizons were defined originally for the Robertson-Walker metrics, and I think my discussion really applies only to models of this general kind. I'm not sure how one would extend the ideas to cover the other type of situations you refer to.

Now, it is possible to show quite generally that if there exists an event horizon (of the type I am considering) in a cosmological model, then purely advanced solutions of Maxwell's equations are not possible for arbitrary ("test") source distributions in that model. An example of such a model is the steady-state universe. We can also show generally that if a particle horizon exists in a cosmological model, then purely retarded solutions of the Maxwell equations are impossible for arbitrary sources. An example of this type is the Einstein–de Sitter model. The de Sitter hyperspherical space-time, which consists of two copies of the steady-state model, has both horizons. One "steady-state" branch goes into the past and the other goes into the future. If we stick them together, we get a complete hypersphere in five dimensions which has both types of horizon. In this case neither purely advanced solutions nor purely retarded solutions are possible for general source behavior.

There is more than one way of looking at the meaning of the purely advanced or retarded solution. The simplest way to visualize the situation for, say, a finite system of particles is to consider the behavior of the field as it proceeds along a null geodesic in space-time into the future or into the past. We can find a characteristic behavior, and we single out one term which behaves as $1/r$, where r is a suitably defined luminosity parameter along this geodesic. We can say that the radiation field is zero if the $1/r$ part vanishes. This procedure will work provided infinity is really at infinity, but if it is either singular or not "metrically" at infinity, we have a bit of trouble.

We examine the field along all null geodesics into past or future. Provided we have a proper infinity, we can ask whether the field falls off as $1/r$ or as $1/r^2$. If it always falls off as $1/r^2$ (or faster) into the past [future] then we can say that there is no incoming [outgoing] radiation. So a purely retarded [advanced] potential is one which has no $1/r$ term along the past [future] light cone. We shall consider a more general approach presently.

One of the big advantages of being able to bring infinity to a finite place is that we can do the initial-value problem for infinity in a per-

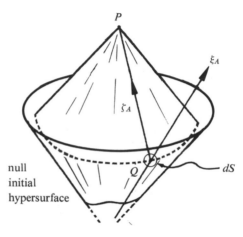

FIGURE III-5

fectly rigorous way. We can specify data on the bounding surface. It is very important whether this surface is a null surface or a spacelike surface. If the surface is null, then we specify one complex number at each point of the surface. In the source-free case, this specification of one complex (that is, two real) numbers at each point of the past cone completely determines the solution. If we have a spacelike surface instead, we need four real numbers at each point, but they are usually rather hard to specify, even in the case of the electromagnetic field. We have in this case six numbers and two constraint equations. In the gravitational case things are still more complicated.

In flat space, a zero rest-mass field can be described according to the following formula, which defines the field at a point P in terms of initial data. In Figure III-5, a *null* initial surface is represented. For arbitrary spin s, we have a spinor $\phi_{AB\ldots}$ which is symmetric, having

$2s$ indices, satisfying $\nabla^{A\dot{P}}\phi_{AB\cdots L}=0$ if $s\geq\frac{1}{2}$, and satisfying $\Box^2\phi=0$ if $s=0$. The expression for $\phi_{AB\cdots L}$ at P, in terms of an integral involving data at the points Q which lie on the intersection of the null cone of P with the null initial surface, is

$$\phi_{AB\cdots L} = \frac{1}{2\pi} \int \frac{1}{r}\zeta_A\zeta_B\cdots\zeta_L\{D\phi - (2s + 1)\rho\phi\}\, dS + \textit{any source terms.}$$

The quantities r, ζ_A, D, ρ, dS, and ϕ are defined by

$$(\overrightarrow{QP})_\mu = r\zeta_A\bar{\zeta}_{\dot{B}}\sigma_\mu{}^{A\dot{B}}; \qquad \xi^A\zeta_A = 1; \qquad D \equiv \xi^A\bar{\xi}^{\dot{B}}\nabla_{A\dot{B}},$$

the spinors ζ_A and ξ_A representing the two null directions orthogonal to dS, with $dS=$ surface area element of 2-dim. intersection surface; $\rho = -\xi^B\nabla_{A\dot{B}}\xi^A$; and $D\xi^A=0$. The initial data quantity on a null initial hypersurface has one complex component:

$$\phi = \phi_{AB\cdots L}\xi^A\xi^B\cdots\xi^L.$$

This formula shows that the (free) field at the point P can be calculated by an integral over the intersection of a null initial surface with the past cone of P. The spinor associated with the null direction along the null cone of P is ζ_A and the quantity ϕ is the initial data quantity, which is just the field contracted with the spinor representing the null direction in the null initial surface. It is the projection of the field down into the initial surface, and it is just one complex number per point of the surface. Note that it is an integral just around an *intersection* of the null cone of P with the initial surface. This treatment works in flat space, and works with suitable modification of the factors in any conformally flat space, so it will work for any isotropic cosmology. If the space were not conformally flat, we would have to consider scattering effects. But since here it is only the data on the intersection of the null cone of P with the initial surface that comes in, we can apply the formula equally well when we have a spacelike initial surface. We can always find a null surface which coincides with a spacelike surface at its intersection with the null cone of P. Thus, if we can find ϕ in terms of the data on the spacelike surface, we can still apply the formula to find the field at P. The spinor ξ_A used here to define ϕ simply corresponds to the null direction (other than that of ζ_A) which is orthogonal to the intersection surface.

Let us now apply the formula when the initial surface is the surface representing past infinity. Then, the initial data quantity ϕ represents what, to an observer at P, would appear to him to be the free incoming radiation. If there is no incoming radiation, the $\phi_{AB \cdots L}$ is given entirely by the source terms. If the free field integral is zero for all points P, then the data must be zero. This means that there is no contribution to the field from the arbitrarily specifiable data at infinity. If we have a charge whose world line cuts the null cone of P at a specified point, then the contribution would come only from that point. More generally, we might have many sources and incoming field. Then we have a contribution from each intersection point of the world line of a charge with the null cone of P ("retarded contributions") together with the free field integral over initial data for the field at infinity ("incoming field").

The idea is that we try to specify initial data at infinity so that, for a retarded field, the free field integral is always zero. This amounts to the quantity ϕ being zero all over the initial surface (and for all allowable choices of ξ^A). When the initial surface is spacelike, this implies that $\phi_{AB \cdots L}$ is zero throughout the initial surface. This is generally impossible if $s > \frac{1}{2}$, since too many conditions (> 4) on the initial data must be satisfied.

X

How do we calculate the field contribution at P from the source? The question is which way we solve the equations, because there is nothing unique about the source terms. We can use a different sort of analysis in the calculation; we can change the contributions which we consider to come from the sources and those from the surface. Perhaps the source terms can be changed by a homogeneous solution. We might say that this is equivalent to changing the incoming condition.

PENROSE

Yes, it is true that I haven't specified how to treat the source terms here, but this doesn't really affect the argument. If we consider, for simplicity, a single charge, in a space with a spacelike past infinity, and work out the field at a point P whose past cone does not even intercept the charge (that is, the charge is outside P's particle horizon), we have the situation illustrated in Figure III-6. This single charge is the only source here, and since the past cone of *P* does not meet the world line of the charge, we would have to say that the entire field at *P* is due to incoming radiation field. Thus, for a purely retarded field, the field at *P* would have to be *zero!* However, it is impossible to arrange that the field be zero at *all* such points *P*, as we can see by examining the field on the cone (shown dotted in the diagram) which is the future cone of the initial point (at infinity) of the world line of the charge. It turns out that there must be a discontinuity in the field along this cone and that the free-field equations are violated at this discontinuity.

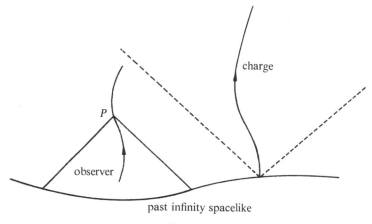

FIGURE III-6

SCHIFF

You could use the fact that the charge can be measured as an integral of field quantities over a sphere surrounding the world line to show this violation.

PENROSE

That's a very good point. A two-sphere surrounding the charge but lying outside the dotted cone would lie entirely in the *zero* field region. The integral giving the charge surrounded would thus be zero. This is a contradiction, so it follows that a purely retarded field is impossible for this situation! This can also be seen if we go back to the original space. Then the world line of the particle extends down forever; it always has a field and its field cannot suddenly cut off at the particle horizon.

BONDI

How do we know that the field at P is all radiation field? I see that the distinction between radiation and Coulomb fields disappears under conformal transformations, since we cannot distinguish any more the $1/r$ from the $1/r^2$ part. But how then do we make the distinction appear again? Cannot the particle move in such a way that it produces only a Coulomb field?

PENROSE

The definition of radiation field is the contribution to the integral which does not come from sources. There are no sources outside the dotted cone, so that the complete contribution is the radiation field outside. The condition that there is no incoming radiation therefore implies that the field must be zero everywhere outside the dotted cone. What looks like a Coulomb field in this picture is radiation in the untransformed field. The conformal transformation does not preserve the concept of radiation field, but the radiation field can be easily identified in the transformed case in terms of field components on the hypersurface representing infinity.

MORRISON

Are you not placing a special regularity condition, a special condition at infinity, on Maxwell's equations, which we normally do not impose?

PENROSE

In a sense, what I do is equivalent to imposing a regularity condition at infinity, but it apparently turns out that any field which looks reasonable in the physical space, and which falls off in the right way, corresponds to a field which is finite on the initial surface, and the formalism can therefore be applied.

HOGARTH

Can you not change a spacelike infinity into a null infinity?

PENROSE

No, because conformal invariance leaves null lines invariant.

HOYLE

I see that the spacelike or null character of the surface affects in a very intimate way the choice of data on the surface. Is this something connected with the general behavior of partial differential equations in the choice of initial data on null cones?

PENROSE

Yes, but this problem is something I am not completely clear about myself.

BONDI

Surely the point is that we can have a boundary between zero and nonzero things only on a null cone. This is a very crucial place, the only place where nonanalytic behavior can take place. This is where the propagation of discontinuities occurs.

PENROSE

This business about having two pieces of data when the suface is null and four when it is spacelike is something that I do not fully understand. There can be a surface which goes along spacelike, then turns and becomes null, then becomes spacelike again. We must then specify four pieces of data first, then two, then four again, as in Figure III-7.

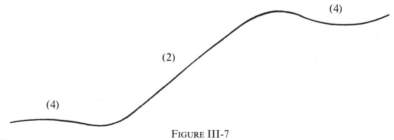

FIGURE III-7

BONDI

The surface gets only the news that is broadcast to a point on it. When we are, say, in the null piece, we travel with one stream of news, and therefore we intercept only one other stream of news. We must think of the information as sliding along with us. We are swimming with the waves. This is quite reasonable.

PENROSE

My problem is more a psychological than a physical one, but perhaps yours is the real explanation.

SCIAMA

This analysis applies only for a finite number of particles. Do you suppose this treatment could be extended to cover the case of an infinite number of particles?

PENROSE

I feel sure that this type of approach would be valuable, but the detailed physical questions soon begin to arise; these worry me. I am trying only to construct conditions which make mathematical sense to me. The situation might be changed if the universe is treated as full of particles; I do not know. My suggestions hold if there are just a few particles with a cosmological background.

IV. Retarded Potentials and the Expansion of the Universe[1]

D. W. Sciama

I am going to talk about the connection between cosmology and retarded potentials, leaving out thermodynamics. This is going to be different from the previous discussions, since I take into account the fact that there are probably sources throughout space. We previously considered matter throughout space, but only in the sense of potential absorbers, whereas I now include radiating sources. The surface temperature of the sources can be measured without specifying the direction of time; all that is required is that the temperature at the surface of a black body should be higher than elsewhere.

We have in a sense an open system, although we consider all the stars at once, because in fact they are strongly linked together. In the case of a static universe, with the density of stars approximately that observed in our locality, the mean free path for a photon is about 10^{19} light years. In this sense we have an open system. Now, it might be said that, since Maxwell electrodynamics is linear, we can discuss the solution for stars locally without considering stars at great distances, but we will see that there is a certain sense in which the theory is nonlinear as regards the way the boundary conditions work. So again we have to consider the whole model at once. Of course it is correct to speak of the normal retarded solution only if certain boundary conditions hold at infinity. It is not clear whether we are allowed to use the ordinary retarded potential or an ordinary advanced potential in the case where sources are distributed throughout space. So I just summarize how the Liénard-Wiechert retarded potential is derived. We shall see that certain details of this derivation cannot be maintained if there are sources throughout space. I use Kirchhoff's theorem, which for simplicity is expressed in terms of a wave equation for a scalar field.

Suppose we are interested in working out the field at the point x at time t.

FIGURE IV-1

$$\phi(x, t) = \int_V \frac{\rho \, dV}{r} + \int_S \phi \, dS.$$

I surround this event with the volume V, an ordinary spatial volume which has a surface S. Then if $\phi(x, t)$ is the field to be computed, it can be set equal to the integral of $\rho \, dV/r$ plus a surface integral. The essential point about the surface integral is that it contains the quantity ϕ. Now, the time at which this integral has to be taken is not the time t, but, in the familiar case, the retarded time. So I will write for short:

$$\phi(x, t) = \int_V \text{ret} + \int_S \text{ret}.$$

However, this can also be written:

$$\phi(x, t) = \int_V \text{adv} + \int_S \text{adv},$$

or

$$\phi(x, t) = \frac{1}{2} \int_V (\text{adv} + \text{ret}) + \frac{1}{2} \int_S (\text{adv} + \text{ret}).$$

One of the most important points is that these are all equal. Kirchhoff's theorem is just a mathematical theorem which says that if the wave equation

$$\Box^2 \phi = \rho$$

is given, then we can represent ϕ at a point x and time t in any of the equivalent forms given above.

The volume integral represents the contribution from the sources within S. The surface integral involves (1) the sources outside S, and (2) possibly source-free radiation coming from infinity. This surface integral satisfies the homogeneous equation inside the volume, and it is related to the F_H which was discussed previously by X. In order to derive, let us say, the retarded solution in the ordinary sense, we are interested in what happens to the surface integral as the volume tends to infinity. That is the essential question which I want to discuss. We have had from Penrose a very elegant discussion of how to deal with boundary conditions at infinity, but I shall discuss the question by very simple physical considerations. To get the retarded potential, we want the retarded surface integral to vanish as V tends to infinity. It vanishes if the following two conditions hold. First, the contribution from the sources outside the volume V tends to zero as V tends to infinity. This I will call for obvious reasons an "Olbers-type condition." The second condition is that there should be no source-free radiation; this can be termed a "Mach-type condition," as it belongs to the philosophy that effects come only from sources. The first condition could be achieved simply by confining the sources to a finite region. The second condition might be achieved by the Sommerfeld radiation condition, which we apply on the past light cone. We then say there is no incoming radiation.

We cannot use either of these devices here to get rid of the surface integral. The first device will not work because we have sources throughout infinite space. The second device is a time-asymmetrical assumption, apart from questions of Wheeler-Feynman electrodynamics, and if we made this assumption, we would be introducing the arrow of time which we are trying to explain.

Since we must discuss the question in the case of a cosmological world model, we may ask first what happens to Kirchhoff's theorem in such a case. I appeal to the conformal flatness of the standard Robertson-Walker models for simplification of the discussion, because in that case the Kirchhoff theorem holds with very little modification. The only modification of the theorem is the introduction of red-shift or blue-shift effects in the surface and volume integrals, depending upon whether we are dealing with the past or the future light cone. The surface S is at rest relative to a comoving coordinate system.

X

You say that Kirchhoff's theorem still works in the conformal model. Does the surface remain fixed? Does the number of stars in the inside remain unchanging with time?

HOYLE

It depends on the cosmology. Stars do move through the surface in some cosmologies and in others they do not. In flat coordinates, the Kirchhoff theorem is true. If we transform a Robertson-Walker model to conformally flat coordinates, Kirchhoff's theorem still holds. The surface S is also fixed in these coordinates.

BERGMANN

The whole purpose of introducing conformally flat surfaces is that we can use non-Minkowski universes and that we can ignore this fact as far as the Maxwell equations are concerned.

PENROSE

It is only the instantaneous position of the surface relative to the observer that comes in.

SCIAMA

Now we want to see what happens to the surface integrals as the volume tends to infinity. We take particular world models to see what happens. Consider the Kirchhoff theorem, where we use purely advanced variables, in the case of the Einstein–de Sitter model. In regard to the Olbers-type condition, the behavior of the volume integral as V increases is dependent upon how bright the sources are in the future. We find that the volume integral diverges because of the blue shift, if a certain condition holds on the luminosity of the stars. This condition is that

$$\operatorname*{Lim}_{t \to \infty} Lt^{5/3} > 0,$$

where L is the luminosity. This is not an immodest rate of cooling; it is not very slow. For instance, a galaxy throughout its whole infinite future would not radiate an infinite amount of energy if this condition holds, so this condition is physically quite realistic.

If the stars and galaxies cool sufficiently slowly for this condition to hold, then the volume integral diverges. One must be careful at this stage in saying that the volume integral diverges. We have supposed so far simply that each source is incoherent with all the other sources, so we now have to consider whether there will be correlated motions between the different sources which will remove this divergence. This happens precisely in the familiar case of the Olbers' paradox in the static model. If we compute the volume integral with incoherent sources, we get a divergence, but what actually happens is that space is filled with radiation of the same temperature as the stars. The interaction between the stars produces phase relations between these sources. Thus interference effects arise that remove the infinity and leave a finite quantity. (Macroscopically we describe this situation by speaking of absorption.) This can be easily seen in terms of solid angles, which is of course the appropriate measure for inverse square laws. In this case, the total solid angle of the observer is filled with stars, and that is enough to give a surface brightness which is the same as that at the surface of a star.

If we want to discuss whether we can save this divergence by the same argument in the case of physical interest, it is sufficient to ask what is the total solid angle subtended by all these sources. The solid angle for the future light cone in the Einstein–de Sitter universe is very small. For the distant future it is far less than 4π, so the sources are not lying behind one another. This is to say that the future absorber is imperfect. In computing the sum we can ignore correlations. There is no screening, and therefore this volume integral really does diverge. Hence the surface integral also diverges. Thus apparently the Olbers' condition is not satisfied, while we may hope that the divergence in the surface integral and the divergence in the volume integral cancel one another to give a finite result, as should be obtained from the equivalent calculation of the retarded field.

Consider now the case of retarded field. We consider the solution in this case to see if the luminosity L of a star is not infinite in the past. But of course this is just the usual situation, where Olbers' condition is satisfied. So we certainly get retarded solutions in the Einstein–de Sitter model. We might say that there is an advanced solution, but we cannot get rid of the surface integrals of an advanced solution, as was the case with the F_H, and the combination of surface and volume integral is equivalent to a retarded solution. Now what happens to the surface integral in the retarded solution? Observation certainly indicates that there is no great amount of source-free radiation incident on the earth. Most of the radiation falling on us, both in the optical and radio parts of the spectrum, can be attributed to sources which we believe on other grounds to exist.

This treatment simply transforms a differential equation into an in-

tegral equation. As was pointed out in previous discussion, the dirt is
picked up by the surface integral. We can always use advanced variables, apart from questions of divergence, but in the case which now
concerns us, we cannot forget the surface integral.

WHEELER

You are talking on the one hand about a point charge and the radiation it gives, and on the other about the wiggling of the charge and the
radiation it produces. Somehow, then, the gears were shifted, and you
switched over to integrating all the stars and such things. I do not yet
see how you shift gears, because each little source has to be treated individually. Then it is not the amplitudes that add, but the intensities.

SCIAMA

The question is about the coherence properties of the source and
about what we can add. In the case of a static universe, we cannot ignore
the correlation between the sources; if we do, the divergence arises
which we know to be wrong, and the phase relations are such that the
correct answer for the surface brightness must be just that corresponding to the surface of a star. We should think of each star, rather than
the atoms in a star, as a point source. Then they do not screen one
another in the Einstein–de Sitter case, since there are no stars lying
behind one another in the future light cone. So the radiation from each
source comes to us independently of the other sources, and we cannot
therefore remove the divergence. Beams of radiation do not overlap
because of the geometry, so it makes no difference whether or not we
square the amplitudes before adding them. But, in any case, what con-
fuses me is that the physical meaning of Kirchhoff's theorem applies in
the standard calculation of brightness of sources in cosmology. We
still have to take account of the sources outside the surface and any
radiation that may exist.

X

The answer is that we can integrate over the amplitude of the sources
only, calculate the result, square it, and then average it over a little interval of space and time. This calculation gives a certain number. This
number presumably can be proved to be equal to the one resulting
from a calculation of the intensity from solid angles and sources. So
your argument about the intensity is not really about a Kirchhoff

integral. It is about another integral which was used to determine the mean-square value of the result of the Kirchhoff integral theorem. The square root of infinity is still infinity, so the presumption is that the Kirchhoff integral diverges if the integral of the intensity diverges.

SCIAMA

Yes. Now, when this condition is satisfied, the Wheeler-Feynman conditions are not satisfied. The reason for this can be seen from the following formula:

$$4\pi\phi = \frac{1}{2}\left(\int_V \mathrm{ret} + \int_V \mathrm{adv}\right) + \frac{1}{2}\left(\int_S \mathrm{ret} + \int_S \mathrm{adv}\right).$$

If we want to deal with volume integrals in effect, the sum of the half-advanced and half-retarded surface integrals must be zero. In the other notation, we say that $F_{in} + F_{out} = 0$. What we actually find is that $\int_S \mathrm{ret} + \int_S \mathrm{adv}$ is not zero, because $\int_S \mathrm{adv}$ is infinite and $\int_S \mathrm{ret}$ is infinite, so the sum cannot be zero. Therefore I suggest that the Wheeler-Feynman conditions are not satisfied if this condition on the brightness of the galaxies holds. If we apply the Wheeler-Feynman conditions in an Einstein–de Sitter model, we find advanced solutions. Now we have cause for worry. The difficulty may be expressed in other terms. The Fokker action principle, which can be taken as the basis of Wheeler-Feynman electrodynamics, is in difficulty because the Fokker action will itself be infinite. If the source-free radiation in the case of advanced fields is not finite, then we do not get a finite solution. We are looking for a finite solution like the actual universe, where L is bounded for the actual sources in the past light cone, so the volume integral in the past light cone is finite. If we add a surface integral that is infinite, then the total field is infinite even if $\int_s \mathrm{ret}$ is finite. In fact, from this point of view, I always use Maxwell's equations and try to make the cosmological boundary conditions decide what the radiation conditions are, or whether the Wheeler-Feynman conditions are satisfied or not.

Now, the Einstein–de Sitter model can be contrasted with the steady-state model. Here the situation is different. First let us consider the retarded form. The source-free contribution must be zero. If it were not, this contribution would increase steadily as we look back into the past. This indefinite monotonic increase would be inconsistent with the steady-state condition. So we have

$$\int_S \text{ret} = 0.$$

And by implication, the Olbers-type condition is satisfied; we get purely retarded solutions, therefore.

BONDI

In the steady-state model the source-free term can be either infinite or zero. Even though you are looking only for a finite solution, the possibility of the infinite solution should be mentioned. Presumably in the advanced case the solution will be infinite.

SCIAMA

This is in fact why I am not making a logically rigorous argument.

Now, considering the advanced case, if we do a simple volume integral, we again get a divergence. But now we must ask about the possible coherence between the sources. In this case the solid angle for the light cone is infinite. In other words, the future absorber is perfect, as originally proved by Hogarth (who also first showed that the future absorber is imperfect in the Einstein–de Sitter model). I find it easier to think in terms of solid angle than to discuss the details of the interaction. The fact that the volume integral diverges is not necessarily worrisome; we have to take into account the correlations. I think that my nonrigorous argument can be justified in terms of calculations.

I now want to show that the purely advanced solution, without the surface integral, is equal to the purely retarded solution. The phase relations in the future, in the advanced case, produce interference so that the future volume integral is precisely equal to the past one. A nonrigorous argument for this is that

$$\lim_{V \to \infty} \left[\int_V \text{adv} - \int_V \text{ret} \right]$$

is source-free, and therefore it is zero. This argument is assailable, since that quantity could be infinite; there could be an infinitely strong wave propagating despite the red shift. It would remain infinitely strong, and the steady-state condition could be satisfied. From the calculations of Hogarth, Hoyle, and Narlikar, however, this quantity is known to be finite, since it is essentially the response of the future absorber which they calculated. Once this quantity is known to be finite, then the argument is perfectly rigorous. We can conclude that if the advanced volume integral is equal to the retarded volume integral, then it follows from the original equations that the advanced surface integral is zero. So we can talk either of purely retarded potentials or of purely advanced potentials, although in the latter case we would have to take into account complicated correlations. This reduces the discussion effectively to the retarded case in which the correlations are relatively unimportant.

We may conclude that the Wheeler-Feynman radiation conditions hold in steady-state theory but not in the "big-bang" cosmologies. In the case of the Einstein–de Sitter model, we had to assume that the galaxies cooled at a slow rate. No such assumption is needed in the steady-state case. There still remain other cases in which cosmological boundary conditions alone suffice to determine the boundary conditions for radiation, and thus also the electrodynamic arrow of time.

SALPETER

You say an individual star or galaxy radiates during a finite time only. This fact means that it has lots of nuclear fuel at one end of its career and little nuclear fuel at the other end. I am curious whether this development is something that can be calculated without having to make any previous assumption about it. Is there some condition which you presumably did not include explicitly at the beginning, but which somehow comes out to make energy conservation consistent?

SCIAMA

I am simply supposing that we have a steady-state distribution of sources with an average luminosity L, wherever we cut it with a light cone. L is, of course, determined by considerations of nuclear fuel and things like that. I suppose it has some finite value in order to be independent of where we look at these sources.

SALPETER

Suppose we have a steady-state cosmology where time goes in the direction in which the model is expanding. Suppose that, instead of creation of diffuse hydrogen atoms, there is creation of white dwarfs made of iron. Everything then presumably would look different.

SCIAMA

L would be zero.

BONDI

In order to get real thermodynamic symmetry, must we not assume that all models contain a lot of dark, obscuring matter as well as sources?

GOLD

Certainly the Einstein–de Sitter universe will merely expand until eventually the radiation is of such long wavelength that something or other absorbs it. After a long while the universe becomes dark.

MORRISON

There probably is a thermodynamic assumption in the steady-state cosmology. The danger is that this has been included unwittingly.

BONDI

The very idea of the steady-state universe is basically a thermo-dynamic idea.

MORRISON

If you try to run the steady-state cosmology backwards, you have trouble.

X

Yes. It is hard to get the hydrogen dispersed enough to suck it out in space at a uniform density. When the model is run backwards, it is hard to find hydrogen to annihilate. It has been created in a nice condition.

GOLD

It is a satisfactory result that it seems hard to run the steady-state model backwards, because that statement means that the motion of the universe itself generates the thermodynamics. Then the steady-state universe will always look like an expanding universe; it does not matter whether we regard the model as expanding or contracting. The thermodynamics will be generated within it so that it looks as if it is expanding.

X

I think that this satisfaction is produced by the special rule of creation that says created matter has to have uniform density throughout space. We all agreed that the initial conditions generate thermodynamics. If the laws of nature were such that matter has to arrange itself in each unit volume at the right moment to be annihilated uniformly every second, then things might well run backwards in the usual sense in order to disperse the mass to be annihilated, so it is just a matter of conditions.

SCIAMA

We would also like to connect thermodynamics in detail to the cosmology by describing how galaxies form, for instance. They probably can form as permanent condensations only by radiating some of their energy to infinity, so that their sense of time must be the same as that for all other things. So galaxies form in the time sense in which the universe is expanding. If they form in a disorderly way, then the initial conditions have something like equal *a priori* probability to cancel. I cannot do such a treatment in detail, since it might be argued that there are so many correlations built into the universe that even when a galaxy forms it is in some special state. In that way it might be possible to link thermodynamics to the cosmology.

GOLD

Let us suppose that all physical theories have some deep reason to be time-symmetrical. Perhaps this reason has escaped us. If Maxwell's equations, which were invented to cover the case of radiation fields only, had to be time-symmetrical, then will they not have symmetry requirements different from those of a theory of radiation involving both particles and fields? For example, if the theory describes only matter with reversible dynamics, then there is no trouble about advanced and retarded potentials when we just throw balls around. When they are thrown, they go in one sense of time. I can look at the events with the time-arrow drawn the other way and the picture is just the same. There is no difficulty. There is a difficulty, however, in drawing the world line of a particle if we must know whether the radiation field had one or another direction. We are unable to look at light between the time of emission and the time of absorption, but we know where the billiard ball is all along its path. So long as there are fields alone in the theory, no problem is encountered; it must be a symmetrical theory for advanced and retarded fields. All this changes when particles are added to the treatment.

In any case, the type of asymmetry associated with retarded potentials for the flow of energy and information arises from a choice or specification. The moment that in addition to the field there is matter in the theory, this particular specification singles out one of the possible solutions. This anisotropy is quite different from the anisotropy of the thermodynamical kind, or that of the expansion of space.

X

I disagree. Light is described as photons, and charges are described as electrons, and these descriptions are all fundamentally the same. In my view, the question of asymmetry has to do with the initial conditions of the world. In specification of the conditions, as Bergmann pointed out, light can be represented mechanically as a bunch of harmonic oscillators even in the classical theory. So we could, if we wish, state the initial conditions of the world by specifying the particles and the light. Then there is no half-advanced, half-retarded theory or anything of the kind, because once we specify the condition of the light at a given time, that defines everything. So there is no important distinction between light and particles.

For certain technical reasons there once was developed a theory of half-advanced and half-retarded potentials, which has a different spirit with regard to light. Light has no independent degrees of freedom in this treatment; the light is always precisely determined by matter. This formal choice was made for various technical reasons having to do with infinities and the classical theory. In this case the connection between the character of the light and the matter is symmetrical. This gives the same physical results as the usual theory, except when the future is transparent, for example. The theory usually gives the same results as those corresponding to advanced or retarded fields, because in most physical circumstances the initial conditions are eventually lost. Even if there were some light initially, it would be absorbed in the walls after a while. The discussions we have had about the relationship between retarded potentials and thermodynamics in an expanding world model have required a particular and arbitrary choice of a theory of electrodynamics, a particular way to discuss light. I believe that the same choice of half advanced and half retarded can be presented also for particles.

In quantum mechanics, there are propagators for the electrons, and the neutrinos, and what not. We have just the same kind of question however we assign the boundary conditions and for whatever particles or fields. I think that the concentration on light in regard to the direction of time is too special. If we choose retarded times only for the solutions of Maxwell's equations, then we are doing something arbitrary and lopsided. We have to make the hypothesis that the field is completely determined by matter, and that there is no such thing as an independent field.

GOLD

The point is that every photon is emitted and also absorbed. Choosing the retarded fields does not create any asymmetry. It is just thermodynamics which gives the asymmetry.

V. Geodesics in Gödel's Universe

S. CHANDRASEKHAR

About fifteen years ago I was present during a discussion at the Institute for Advanced Study when Gödel gave a talk entitled "Time in General Relativity." In this talk, Gödel wrote down a particular solution of Einstein's field equations which had the property that the velocity field is rotational, in the sense that the covariant curl of the velocity field is different from zero. Gödel said that on this metric an observer should be able to travel along geodesics in a way such that he could visit his past and influence the past in some way. Later on, of course, Gödel published this work, and in an article he wrote for the volume *Albert Einstein, Philosopher-Scientist*, he repeated these statements. I remember that in the discussion Einstein said that he did not like these results. That was about all he would say. Figure V-1 is a particular diagram which Gödel drew on that occasion and about which he made the following remark: Suppose we consider an observer traveling along geodesic *A* with time measured in a way such that he gets older with time. Then at a particular point he could depart from *A* and travel along another geodesic *B* for a sufficient length of time such that he comes back and visits his earlier time.

This statement has remained in the literature for more than fourteen years, but about a year or two ago I had the curiosity simply to integrate geodesics in Gödel's metric. It turns out that in this Gödel metric we can introduce coordinates which we might describe as cylindrical polar coordinates. It is possible to have circular orbits in this metric, but so long as we insist that ds^2 is one sign or zero, then these circular orbits, or geodesics, have a certain maximum radius, and along this orbit of maximum radius, $ds^2 = 0$. As long as the circular orbits which are used in this diagram are those for which ds^2 is positive, then the result is that if the observer travels along a circular orbit, he will come back not into his past, but only into his future. The kind of thing which

68

Gödel suggested is possible only when these circular orbits exceed the maximum radius.

If I have interpreted Gödel's remarks correctly, and if we first choose the sense of time along one geodesic and follow that sense along the others, then it would seem that the kind of phenomenon which Gödel had in mind does not in fact occur in this metric. The fact that the situation which he describes is impossible with this metric does not disprove this possibility altogether in the framework of general relativity. It

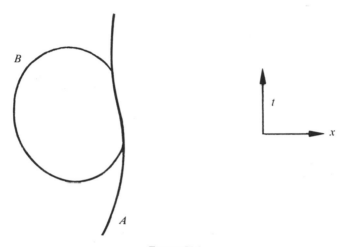

FIGURE V-1

would be very nice to be able to show the general impossibility of closed time-like geodesics, but it seems to me that the particular example he gave is not valid.

Gödel chose solutions of the field equations with the cosmical constant different from zero. However, it is not difficult to construct solutions having a similar property, in which the cosmical constant is zero. Of course, working out special examples does not prove the general theorem, but for the special cases which we have worked out, the ability to visit the past does not seem to exist.

BONDI

When you speak of the possible proof of the theorem that trips into the past cannot be made, do you have in mind the case of empty space or a case in which material sources are somehow restricted?

CHANDRASEKHAR

The field equations which we used have a term for incoherent matter. The energy-momentum tensor of the right-hand side of the equation describes a pure velocity, so in a sense the laws correspond to the field equations of cosmology.

BONDI

I would have guessed that a distinction always arises in which we can have on one side of the equation terms for empty space and for matter in which there is one timelike eigenvector, and on the other side things that are otherwise, that is matter with a definable velocity. If this were done, then perhaps the events described in Gödel's suggestion would happen only when the most appalling type of matter is put into the field equations.

RINDLER

Leaving aside the question of whether the existence of closed time-like lines in a world model, such as Gödel's, is embarrassing, there is no question that we can construct much simpler models which satisfy Einstein's field equations everywhere and which do contain such lines, and in which an observer can consequently "travel into his past." Perhaps the simplest model of this kind would consist of flat Minkowski space subdivided into equal hypercubes whose opposite (hyper-) faces are identified, that is, a hypertorus. The lines x, y, $z =$ constant are timelike, closed, and finite under this topology. Similarly, the variant of de Sitter space (corresponding to a negative cosmological constant) which can be described as the hypersurface $x^2 + y^2 + z^2 - u^2 - w^2 = -a^2$ immersed in pseudo-Euclidean five-space with metric $dx^2 + dy^2 + dz^2 - du^2 - dw^2$ allows finite closed timelike geodesics; for example, the waist-circle of the hyperboloid $u^2 + w^2 - x^2 = a^2$ with y, z constant. But this situation can be remedied by considering, instead of this space, its covering space, corresponding to the hyperboloid being regarded as an infinite scroll and then unrolled, just as the hypertorus can be "unrolled" into ordinary Minkowski space. It can also be remedied by considering the duration of the substratum to be finite—from big bang at one point of the waist-circle to collapse at the antipode. Perhaps such remedies are possible whenever closed timelike lines exist. To illustrate a related embarrassment in some cosmological models, one might mention the elliptic form of de Sitter space, in which, no matter how time is defined, an observer can always travel from "normal" regions into regions where time runs backwards relative to his own continuous arrow of time.

X

I would conjecture that if the equations are taken to be $G_{\mu\nu} = T_{\mu\nu}$, closed timelike world lines could occur if $T_{\mu\nu}$ in places were negative, or the equivalent of this. Things like negative-energy sources might make disturbances in other places.

I believe we have an example in which an observer comes out of a region before he goes in. There is a metric of charge and mass-point, called the Nordstrøm metric. If an observer goes straight in with a finite angular momentum, he goes through the singularity analogous to the $2m$ singularity in the Schwartzschild metric. Deeper down we have another place where the signature changes again, because the form

$$1 - \frac{2m}{r} + \frac{q^2}{r^2}$$

has two zeros. I do not believe that this metric really represents the limit of the metrics in which the charge is taken smaller and smaller. The observer passes both zeros, and then keeps right on going and comes out again through the surface. It turns out that he must come out of the surface before he went in.

When this "backwards" result was obtained, I was worried about causality. I thought that if there were a negative mass somewhere, then anything could happen. This can be understood qualitatively in the following way. Suppose that we have a finite charge of radius a and that we want the field to be so strong that the object has a mass. The field outside the point charge is q/r^2 and the energy density is q^2/r^4. Now the whole object has a mass m, and far away from it all we observe about it is its mass. The gravity has as its source the energy density, and also the stress tensor components, and so forth. As we come close to the charge, we must take away the mass which corresponds to the energy as well as the stress terms, and so on. Now, we calculate how much the mass is from r to infinity, and, within numerical factors, this mass is $\int_r^\infty (q^2/r^4) r^2 dr = q^2/r$. In a certain sense, to get the potential, we should not take the mass over r; we should first find the field and then integrate, but that gives another numerical coefficient. So the mass outside is the total mass minus the energy which is outside, with the right coefficients. And then the general formula for potentials is this total mass divided by r,

$$\frac{m - q^2/r}{r}.$$

Generally speaking, the metric is 1 minus the potential, or

$$1 - \frac{2m}{r} + \frac{q^2}{r^2}.$$

But r can get so small that the mass makes this quantity negative. We want to make it positive again. The term q^2/r^2 must compensate. The mass is a total energy, and as we go inwards, the energy which is outside is being taken away from that, and we can keep on going until we have taken out more energy than we had to begin with.

In other words, the physical situation which could cause this result would be one in which we put a charge and a mechanical mass at the origin. We calculate so that there is a total mass m outside which is equal to the electromagnetic part. Now, this quantity depends on the radius. As we make the radius smaller and smaller we keep m fixed; that means we must put in a negative m_0. So in this sequence of examples, the radius eventually becomes so small that the object really must have a negative central mass. These difficulties of causality arise when we have a negative t_{44} somewhere in the system.

BERGMANN

I am afraid you have played with the energy concept in too naïve a fashion.

X

I understand that I have. I say things in this way in order to give a qualitative idea that the energy concept is the cause of the trouble. It is possible to use imprecise reasoning to get ideas. Now the question is whether this discussion is good or not. We have a finite sequence of problems having no singularities in any of them except the limiting one. As the metric approaches that of a point charge, the m will have to go up with q^2 so that it becomes effectively positive. Then the second change of sign can never occur for any of the real problems in the sequence. I think this might even be true.

WHEELER

I do not agree with this line of reasoning because the initial-value problem for this case (Reissner-Nordstrøm) has a perfectly regular geometry, although it has an unusual topology. After a finite time the geometry becomes singular. We formulate in different ways the reason it does so, but we agree that it does become singular; so we should agree that this metric is not acceptable.

We are interested to know why this singularity comes about. In contrast with the pure Schwarzschild case, in which the throat of the metric shrinks to nothing and becomes singular, the Reissner-Nordstrøm throat has lines of electric force threading through it. The Faraday-Maxwell elasticity of these lines of force keeps the throat from collapsing. The infalling throat "bounces" and re-expands, and continues to oscillate in radius again and again. Therefore one might think that there would not be a singularity. In agreement with this reasoning, the singularity is indeed somewhere other than at the throat.

This "bouncing," or periodical behavior of the throat, leads us to the question about whether an observer can come back to a past segment of his world line. Such a universe would normally be described as a periodically repeating universe. Birkhoff's theorem states, however, that there are no periodic spherically symmetric solutions of Einstein's equations. This proof therefore says that we cannot have such a universe, except a trivial one which has the topology of the four-torus.

BERGMANN

Yes, but that is certainly a valid solution. We should not disregard it just because it happens to be locally flat. Suppose we consider a locally flat Minkowski universe, but then mess up its topology by the method which people use in solid-state physics. We make a "periodicity tube," but we make it in four dimensions instead of three. Then it is certainly possible to find two timelike geodesics which intersect at more than one point. For one of the two particles the second encounter is later and for the other it is earlier.

WHEELER

But if we have even one particle in this space, then there is no longer a solution.

BERGMANN

That is right. It is not a stable solution.

MISNER

But this "NUT" (Newman-Unti-Tamburino) solution of the Einstein equations, in which $R_{\mu\nu}=0$ everywhere, actually includes closed timelike geodesics. On the other hand, it includes many unphysical features. It does not seem to be stable against introduction of matter, so I am not ready to take it very seriously.

VI. Infinite Red-Shifts in General Relativity

C. Misner

I would like to talk about how people get out of touch with each other. One example of this situation occurs in the horizons that appear in cosmology. Two observers who were able to talk to each other head off in different directions and eventually there is no longer a possibility of communication between them. Another question is whether it is possible for the universe genuinely to fission. If so, we would get the sort of behavior depicted in Figure VI-1, where the universe we started

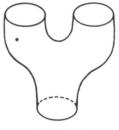

FIGURE VI-1

with evolves into two. But I shall ignore these cosmological questions and talk about a local situation in which two observers can get out of touch with each other. This situation occurs in the Oppenheimer-Snyder problem of continuing stellar collapse.[1] The problem has become interesting recently from a number of points of view, and we shall try to review it here. In particular, there is a geometrical picture of this Oppenheimer-Snyder solution, given by D. L. Beckedorff,[2] which I will summarize.

How can violent stellar collapse come about in the real world? When stars evolve and get cold, the radiation pressure is no longer able to support them, and they begin to collapse. Eventually, the star might become merely a Fermi sea, whose pressure prevents collapse. As the

75

star crushes down, there is less space, but the electrons still need the same number of quantum states. These fermions then fill up more of the momentum space, since they have less configuration space available to them. The work it takes for them to fill up momentum space determines the pressure that resists further collapse. As we fill a state with momentum p, we have to supply an energy $E = p^2/2m$, and this determines the force law. Eventually, as things crush down, the electrons become relativistic and $E = pc$. The difference between the square power of p and the linear power of p in the nonrelativistic and relativistic cases is a crucial one. It turns out that when we work with the relativistic force law, there is no equilibrium. Either the system will expand and continue expanding as long as this relativistic relation holds, or else it will contract and continue contracting as long as this formula holds. This depends entirely on the total mass of the system; the critical mass is given, for an electron gas, by the Chandrasekhar limit,[3] which says that there cannot be equilibrium of a white-dwarf-type star of degenerate electron gas having total mass greater than about 1.5 solar masses.

What happens after the star collapses? If the electrons are crushed onto most of the protons, a degenerate neutron gas results. But what happens when the neutrons become relativistic? The critical mass in this case is smaller; it is on the order of .65 solar masses.[4] Above that there is no equilibrium supported by a neutron gas. Still, equilibrium can be found for other possibilities, such as those in which the star breaks up into smaller pieces, or in which angular momentum prevents the collapse. Both these possibilites are very real; both shedding of mass and spinning are known to be effects in stars. If we ignore these, it is because we cannot calculate them. My own feeling is that there is not an equilibrium in these circumstances. We should look forward to a continuing collapse.

We have been talking in terms of the degenerate-electron-gas equation of state, and the degenerate-neutron-gas equation of state. Wheeler has discussed also a detailed equation of state,[5] and Ambartsumian[6] has discussed the problem of composition of superdense stars. After the collapse, neutron levels are built up, and it becomes cheaper energetically to produce mesons, and so on, rather than to fill higher energy neutron levels. Therefore we have to ask about elementary particles before we can determine the equation of state. However, we can also try to do the problem in the complete limit. Suppose we consider an incompressible fluid. By "incompressible fluid" is meant the following: we look for equilibrium situations, and the pressure is to be whatever is required to permit them. The density, which is the constant ρ occurring in the formula for $T_{\mu\nu}$, is specified beforehand.

We are then considering the standard and well-known problem of the interior Schwarzschild solution.[7] We still have a limit in this case; if there is too much mass in a given region, then we cannot find an equilibrium solution.[8] I will do the work in detail later, but the result is that the density which we assume in such a case has to satisfy

$$\rho \leq \left(\frac{M_\odot}{M}\right)^2 \times 1.4 \times 10^{16} \frac{\text{gm}}{\text{cm}^3}, \tag{1}$$

where M is the mass of the object and $M_\odot$ is the mass of the sun. We find an equilibrium solution of the Einstein equation for a mass M of incompressible fluid only when this condition is satisfied. At the center we have infinite pressure; in the $T_{\mu\nu}$ this implies an infinite curvature scalar of some kind. The separation of positive and negative energy states goes to zero at the center.

All the limits found by the particular equations of state ultimately fall below those given by the inequality (1) above. We may draw some conclusions from this inequality. If there is a big enough mass, the collapse can begin at low densities. So these elementary-particle spectra, nuclear-force laws, hard cores, and so forth are irrelevant to this question, in principle. In particular, let us put in a mass of $10^8 \, M_\odot$ which just cancels the factor of 10^{16}. A body of $10^8 \, M_\odot$ gathered together in one sphere cannot attain a zero-temperature equilibrium unless the density is less than that of water. So a very ordinary density would come about in this case.

MORRISON

You must say something about the localization of the density, because the density of real matter is not really anything like this. It is on the order of either 10^{18} or zero.

MISNER

Yes. Here we have assumed constant density.

MORRISON

Grainy matter is somehow singular. What will we see at short distances inside this object?

MISNER

If we put in a very small mass, such as the mass of the proton, then the density limit is very high; the density of the proton does not exceed it.

BERGMANN

This problem is more relevant to the collapse of a galaxy; for a galaxy, 1.4 gm/cm^3 is quite a hefty density. It is about 10^{30} times the normal density.

MISNER

I am not claiming that these are normal densities. I am just claiming that we do not have to worry about quantum effects. This is not nuclear matter. The answer to this problem does not in principle rely on the elementary-particle spectrum, unless we want to discuss collapse of relatively small objects of less than one solar mass. And for values of the order of one solar mass, densities somewhat higher than that of nuclear matter arise. So this case is on the borderline as regards our knowing or not knowing the equation of state.

The main thing that concerns us is the nonequilibrium solution when collapse begins. Only an ideal case is known—the case in which there is spherical symmetry and zero pressure; this is a free-falling collapse.

The question of hard nuclear cores has arisen in connection with the "borderline" case of collapse of stars having about one solar mass. S. Weinberg[9] has in this connection considered world models instead of stars, which is really the same question. He was concerned with oscillating universes, and how dense they can get. If we want the model to bounce rather than collapse, we must have attractive nuclear cores. The introduction of hard nuclear cores does not make the model bounce. Repulsive forces make the model collapse faster, because repulsive forces correspond to positive potential energies. Positive potential energies produce more energy and more gravitational attraction. When the limit has been passed, the hard core makes the object contract even faster. What we need therefore is a short-range, deep potential for attraction, if the object, whether world model or star, is to bounce.

Now we consider the state which can be treated as an exact solution in our idealization. We obtain it by putting together several solutions which we are familiar with. The Friedman world model turns out to describe properly the geometry corresponding to the state of pressure-free collapsing dust inside the star. To get a model representing the whole metric for the collapsing star, we match the Friedman metric onto the exterior Schwarzschild solution, which we follow in Kruskal's representation.

The metric for the *interior Schwarzschild solution* is[10]

$$ds^2 = R^2(dX^2 + \sin^2 X \, d\Omega^2) - \tfrac{3}{2}(\cos X_0 - \tfrac{1}{3}\cos X) \, dt^2$$
$$\text{where} \quad d\Omega^2 = d\theta^2 + \sin^2 \theta \, d\varphi^2. \tag{2}$$

This model is spherically symmetric, so we use $d\Omega^2$ as the metric on the sphere; we do not need to write out those angles explicitly all the time. The space part of the interior Schwarzschild solution is a three-dimensional sphere, and X is the third angle in addition to the usual two, and $\sin^2 X$ is the radius of a two-dimensional sphere of constant X. Then R is the radius of the three-dimensional sphere, because the interior of the Schwarzschild model looks like a section of a sphere within limiting angle X_0; we use the metric (2) only out to a certain maximum radius, determined by X_0, (Figure VI-2). This section of the three-dimensional

FIGURE VI-2

sphere filled with matter is to be joined to the exterior Schwarzschild solution. Because of the factor $\tfrac{1}{3}$ in the metric, we need $\cos X_0 > \tfrac{1}{3}$ in order to preserve the correct signature, so we can get only a moderate size angle X. The limit density which we wrote down is based on this fact, so if the density exceeds the limit, g_{00} possibly goes to zero at the center. The pressure, which is given by a formula which involves the same thing in the denominator, goes to infinity.

We can picture this whole Schwarzschild solution by drawing the curvature of the solution imbedded somehow in another space. Instead of having the exterior Schwarzschild solution go on towards its singularity, we stop it and fill it in with a section of the three-dimensional sphere where the matter lies (Figure VI-3).

The *Friedman solution* has essentially the same geometry as the three-

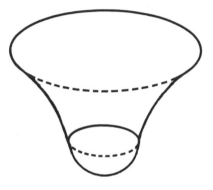

FIGURE VI-3

dimensional sphere, but this solution uses all of the sphere. This world model is filled with dust at zero pressure and uniform density; it differs locally from the Schwarzschild interior not in the instantaneous picture of the geometry, but in the dynamical picture. The Friedman universe is a collection of dust that expands and then collapses. So the Friedman universe has the same sort of spatial metric as the Schwarzschild interior, but with a time-dependent radius $R(t)$, again with three angles representing the three-dimensional sphere, $d\Sigma$.

$$ds^2 = R^2(t)\,d\Sigma^2 - dt^2$$
$$d\Sigma^2 = dX^2 + \sin^2 X\,d\Omega^2. \tag{3}$$

If we choose proper time for t we can get $g_{00}=1$, or at least a spatial constant for g_{00}, which otherwise could or could not be time-dependent. So $R^2 d\Sigma^2$ represents spatial sections, or three-dimensional spheres. The geometry is the same as before. Again we have the same angle X, but now it has the full range of values, and the radius of this sphere expands and collapses according to a certain law, which is a cycloid curve if there is no pressure.

The next familiar solution to consider is the *exterior Schwarzschild solution* in the Kruskal representation. With this we can know what is happening at the singularity. We need to know this because in stellar collapse, the matter follows geodesics and in finite proper time falls right into the Schwarzschild singularity at $r=2m$.

The following is the Schwarzschild metric in standard coordinates.

$$ds^2 = - \frac{dt^2}{\frac{2m}{t} - 1} + \left(\frac{2m}{t} - 1\right) dz^2 + t^2 d\Omega^2 \qquad (4)$$

I merely changed the names: r is usually written where we write t; t is usually written where we write z. What does the metric look like for $r<2m$? This form is appropriate for the case in which we are going towards what is normally called $r=0$. I simply point out that for these small values of Schwarzschild's r, which we call t, the signature is such that the r (our t) has a time interpretation. What is the sort of geometrical picture here? The space sections are the terms in dz^2 and $d\Omega^2$, and we see that as t goes to zero, the coefficient of dz^2 becomes positively infinite. So the z dimensions are stretching in the z direction as t goes to zero. The cross sections, which are spheres, are collapsing. So the geometrical picture is that of a cylinder, with z measured along it, and with cross sections being ordinary two-dimensional spheres. It is just like a piece of rubber tubing being pulled out as the time coordinate changes. It has cylindrical symmetry, because z does not appear anywhere else. The object stretches in one dimension and collapses in two. The infinite curvature arises when cross sections have zero radius.

Now, this solution ought to have something to do with the normal exterior Schwarzschild metric, which is a static situation, because if we follow the equation of a geodesic, it goes from $r>2m$ to $r<2m$. How do we put these solutions together? We introduce a single system which covers both sides of the "singularity." Kruskal[11] introduced coordinates u and v, by the following sort of transformation.

$$u^2 - v^2 = (r - 1)e^r$$

$$\frac{u}{v} = \tanh t$$

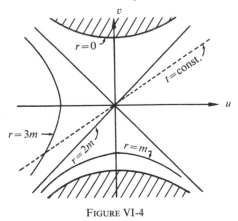

FIGURE VI-4

I do not guarantee every detail of these equations; we may need factors of $2m$ and such quantitative features. The variables r and t are now the same as the standard Schwarzschild r and t, and if we draw the u, v plane, we see that $r = 2m$ corresponds to $(r-1)e^r = 0$, or $u = \pm v$ (Figure VI-4). Standard surfaces, $t = $ constant, the spacelike surfaces in the normal exterior Schwarzschild solution, are $u/v = $ constant, so they are slanted lines through the origin of this diagram. An observer who is on a satellite orbiting around the star, or in any orbit of constant r, lies on curves $u^2 - v^2 = $ constant, which are hyperbolas. On the other hand, r is a singular function of u and v at $r = 0$, and the Schwarzschild curvature invariants become infinite there. Then $r = 0$ corresponds to $u^2 - v^2 = -1$, which is another hyperbola. We never get into the shaded region because at $r = 0$ we already have infinite curvature. The metric is roughly some function of r times $du^2 - dv^2$, plus the other coordinates $r^2 d\Omega^2$:

$$ds^2 = \frac{e^{-r}}{r}(du^2 - dv^2) + r^2\, d\Omega^2. \tag{5}$$

The important feature of this metric is that the light cones are at $45°$ in the u, v plane, so we can conveniently discuss causality questions by using this diagram, so long as the light has no angular momentum and goes radially inwards or outwards.

The transformation laws are such that the metric is nonsingular throughout the entire region that is unshaded. It includes both areas $r > 2m$ and $r < 2m$, so we can see both of them. The part just next to the shaded region is the part which can be described as a collapsing cylinder. That is the $r < 2m$ region. Below that is the familiar $r > 2m$ region. The metric at $u = v$ shows no singular behavior whatever, so it gives somehow a smooth transition in the diagram between one of these behaviors and the other. I do not know how to think of that transition, but it is there.

How can we visualize the content of Figure VI-4? We should look at the geometry of this spacelike surface, $t = 0$ where $v = 0$. We can think of the surface as a succession of concentric spheres, each of radius r. We get some idea of how it looks by seeing how r varies with u. We start out with $r = \infty$ where $u = -\infty$; we then come to a sphere of a certain finite radius $r = 2m$ at $u = 0$, and we keep on going until $r = \infty$ again at $u = +\infty$. So this sequence of concentric spheres starts with large ones, comes to those of small finite size, and then comes to large ones again. This suggests Figure VI-5.

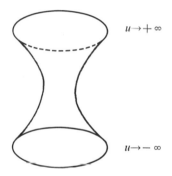

$u \to + \infty$

$u \to - \infty$

FIGURE VI-5

Now the entire metric will describe the dynamics of this. Suppose that an observer is at the neck of Figure VI-5. By looking at Figure VI-4, he interprets the $u = 0$ line to be a geodesic as shown. It is a timelike geodesic, since light cones are at 45°. So an observer who starts at the neck will eventually end up at $r = 0$. If we draw a spacelike surface $v = \text{const.} > 0$ through him and ask for a description of this surface, we see a set of concentric spheres with $r = +\infty, \cdots 3m, 2m, m, 2m, 3m, \cdots +\infty$. We get qualitatively the same picture, Figure VI-5, as before, except that the minimum circumference does not correspond to a radius of $2m$ but to a smaller radius. Therefore what we find is that this space is essentially dynamic, and that the center is collapsing. We will tie this central collapse to the collapse of the star by throwing out some of the empty space and replacing it with an interior solution.

Figure VI-4 can also be used to visualize the causality relationships. We need to consider light rays, the radial null geodesics. Consider an "orbiting" observer at 1 who stays on curve $r > 2m$, as in Figure VI-6. He can send a light signal which goes into the $r < 2m$ region. If, however, this light ray hits another observer at 2, who is in the $r > 2m$ region,

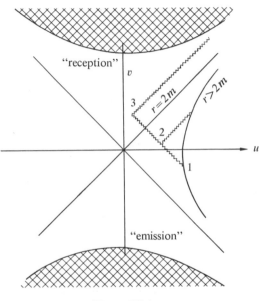

FIGURE VI-6

the first observer can get a reply. Observer 2 can send another message back which would intercept the first observer's orbit $r > 2m$. So there can be communication between these two observers. Suppose however that the light ray goes on farther before it hits someone who replies, say, at some event 3. A message sent back never gets into the region $r > 2m$ again! So their times have become disconnected. The phenomenon shows that there exists here an horizon of a type similar to that in cosmology; two observers who were originally in communication get out of communication. The observer following the radial geodesic cannot send a message to the observer orbiting on $r > 2m$ after the former attains $r = 2m$.

Of course, this solution has time symmetry. Messages from the $r < 2m$ region with $v > 0$ can never get out although messages can be received from outside. If we consider the lower part of the diagram, we see that an observer in the region $r < 2m$ but $v < 0$ can send messages out of this region, but he can never receive any from the exterior region. So we may label the regions, "emission" and "reception." For $v < 0$, the region can emit but not receive messages from the outside, and for $v > 0$ the $r < 2m$ region can receive but not transmit communications to the outside.

One other thing that will be useful to us is to notice what happens in this diagram if we want to change the zero of time. Suppose there is an observer far out, and difficult to watch. Suppose we want to bring him back. We can do this just by changing the zero of time. Changing the zero of time will change the v/u ratio, but at constant r it keeps $u^2 - v^2$ invariant. So a shift in the zero of time in the standard Schwarzschild coordinates corresponds to a Lorentz transformation in the u, v plane, namely a linear transformation which preserves the quadratic form $u^2 - v^2$. To ask what happens to a given geodesic if we look at it from a different vantage point, we make such a pseudo-Lorentz transformation to obtain an equivalent geodesic differently situated in the diagram.

For the case of a collapsing star, we must take an exterior Schwarzschild solution as initial conditions. This is a section of a sphere representing uniform density of matter. If there is enough pressure, the geometry will stay static. If there is too much matter present, even infinite pressure will not prevent a collapse. But, under any circumstances, if the pressure is "turned off" the assembly will collapse. These initial conditions also represent, with changes of scale, the way the geometry looks all during the collapse. How do we represent these conditions, say, on the Kruskal diagram? At $t = 0$ we accept the exterior Schwarzschild solution outside a certain radius. Inside, we erase it and match up the piece of a Friedman sphere with it. So part of the Kruskal diagram stops being meaningful at $t = 0$. What will be the time development from these initial conditions? If there is no pressure, the particle that is on the surface falls on a geodesic. There are no forces, and the motion describes a geodesic for both the exterior and the interior metric. So we must throw away the shaded part of the diagram and replace it by some other solution, as in Figure VI-7.

We know what the exterior behavior looks like. We know that just before the radial geodesics cross $r = 2m$, we can see the surface of the collapsing star. It emits light which we can see for a while, but eventually any light it emits no longer escapes. Even if there is some finite temperature at the surface of the star, but not enough pressure to interfere with the collapse, radiation cannot get out after the star has collapsed past $r = 2m$. This represents an infinite red-shift, or infinite Doppler shift. Actually, we have a combination of gravitational red-shift and Doppler

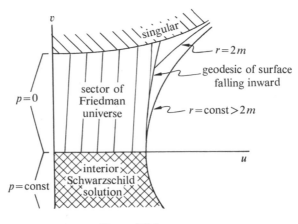

FIGURE VI-7

shift in this case. It is perhaps not meaningful to try to separate the two effects.

For the external observer, the time is constant along radial lines of this diagram. As the radial line swings up toward $u = v$, we have $t \to \infty$. So it takes an infinite length of time for the particle to disappear. An observer at constant r reaches $t \to \infty$ before noting the disappearance of the particle falling in. The observer outside sees it getting redder and redder.

Now, the method of making sure that we have the whole solution under control is to match a solution for the exterior, represented in Schwarzschild or Kruskal coordinates, to an interior solution. We know that the borderline representing the falling particles must be a geodesic. So we know what border we require in that part of the diagram. We now put a border on the Friedman model, a border which must be, as we know from the previous discussions of the Friedman universe, the geodesics at constant angle X. So we choose some fixed constant angle X; the particle sitting there follows the geodesic as the radius of the whole model changes. So a geodesic bounding-surface is made by taking a part of the whole model. We also know the geometry for this object. The question now arises whether or not they match.

The first matching condition is that the circumferences of the two surfaces be the same as a function of time. We see that the formula for the circumference of the surface in the Schwarzschild solution is given by the cycloid formula for r and t, where t is the proper time. We find just the same thing for the other solution. We readily verify that they both have the same law of collapse. But this is only matching the metric on the surfaces, so to speak, and we know that for a second-order differential equation to match, both metric and first derivative must match. How do we match the first derivative? Oppenheimer and Snyder of course represented the whole thing in one coordinate system and matched the first derivatives. This is awkward because we then have to definite strange coordinate systems in order to be able to see the whole picture. A way to avoid that technique is through matching what is called the "second fundamental form." This form is an intrinsic geometric characterization of the surface which has the same information in it as the first derivative, but which is independent of coordinate system. We can compute it independently from inside and outside using the appropriate coordinates. We can check whether the two pieces fit together by checking intrinsic geometrical properties of the interface. One of the properties is the metric on the interface and the other is the way the metric is embedded in its neighboring geometry, and this property is measured by the second fundamental form. Beckedorff simply computed the second fundamental form from outside and from inside and verified that they agreed. So we know that these two solutions do in fact match together. Anyhow, it is best to think of all the relationships from this Kruskal diagram. I like the diagram because I can see how it matches up the standard exterior Schwarzschild region to the interior regions. We cannot use this diagram if we use the other approach.

The total solution gives us just the picture we described at first, but tells us that the radius of the interface, the circumference of the inner sphere, follows the law of collapse which we mentioned. The density is still moderate while we use the equation of state. We know that we can stop worrying about mesons, and so on, being produced until the surface of the star gets across this critical $r = 2m$ surface and vanishes.

MORRISON

But now we have no problem, because if there is a meter stick half outside and half inside the interior region, then one end does not experience the forces on the other end.

X

A meter stick is too long!

MORRISON

Yes, but suppose there is an atom at the boundary $r = 2m$. What happens?

X

As the atom crosses $r = 2m$, it is all right locally. Only when the atom is seen from infinity could this give trouble.

MISNER

Now we want to see what happens when the curvature gets high. We have followed the star until it went out of sight. We followed it for $t = \infty$, as far as we are concerned. The collapse at $r = 2m$ is still at moderate density; there are only moderate curvatures, and no quantum mechanics has to be worried about. But according to the picture we have constructed, the collapse continues by itself. Eventually the assembly attains infinite density and infinite curvature, and we will have these problems. Will they bother us? Will they change the solution? The answer is that they will not. We have a uniqueness theorem due to Stellmacher which says that if we have the initial data for such a solution which are given on a spacelike surface, then the solution is unique. It depends only on the initial data within its past light cone, which is at angle 45° in our diagram. Now, to an observer at a point where $r < 2m$, the physics can depend on the high density which develops, but for an $r > 2m$ region, the physics is uniquely determined by the equation of state of the material before it reaches high density. If the stars explode and emit huge amounts of radiation inside $r = 2m$, none of this can ever affect what is seen outside. All radiation, all the new elementary particles or anything else that arises in this object, will be entirely contained.

Suppose, however, that we inquire how the collapsing star looks to an observer at $r > 2m$ as $t \to \infty$. We use a Lorentz transformation in the u, v plane. This is equivalent to a change of the time origin of the Schwarzschild coordinates. The geodesic describing the surface of the star is changed into another geodesic. This geodesic tends asymptotically toward the light cone $v = -u$. Eventually the star collapses at the speed of light. So as $t \to \infty$, the figure looks just like the first one we drew for the u, v plane, Figure VI-4, except that the region to the left (or below) the null line $v = -u$ is to be replaced by an interior solution, or ignored.

HOYLE

Does it worry you that this disaster as seen from the inside happens in a finite proper time, in a very short proper time in fact?

MISNER

Well, it suggests to me that I would prefer not to get into this situation!

ROBINSON

An observer in the Schwarzschild solution whose coordinates r, θ, ϕ are fixed is not in a state of free fall. He is in an accelerated state, and the gravitational force on him is constant. On the other hand, suppose that there is an observer in Minkowski space who is given a constant acceleration. If that observer carries out just the same series of experiments with light signals, he encounters the same difficulty as the observer in the Schwarzschild metric does. Of course this does not dispose of the "disaster" which Misner describes, because the observer moving around the center of the object is in free fall, and will also observe the "disaster." But the general argument must be based on geodesics because otherwise time could be fragmented by artificial means.

VII. Three-Dimensional Geometry as a Carrier of Information about Time

J. A. WHEELER

The idea of treating the interaction between one particle and another as a process that takes place with a certain finite time delay is after all only a natural and simple generalization of what we do in ordinary Newtonian mechanics where interactions are considered to be instantaneous. As is well known, the treatment can be made without using half-advanced and half-retarded potentials if we discuss the topic in terms of thermodynamic equilibrium, or statistical fluctuations. We select one particle, and so that it may be more easily seen, we think of it as perhaps larger than the others, but otherwise in no way different. If we plot its energy as a function of time, we have the natural statistical fluctuations about the value of $\frac{3}{2}kT$. Occasionally the fluctuations are larger than normal, but then they relapse back to the normal value. We know that the relapse in a case like this can be discussed in terms of the idea of the friction coefficient. We think of radiation damping as being analogous to just such a friction coefficient, but we think of the development of the fluctuation as being something which can be described by the negative of the friction coefficient. We therefore say in the problem of ordinary statistical equilibrium that the fluctuations can be discussed in terms of the friction coefficient.

But when we consider the case of the universe as a whole, the idea of applying any such reasoning to it is appalling. The statistical fluctuation would have to be fantastic in order to produce a systematically one-sided entropy change in a system so gigantic. The entropy change is found to be one-sided in every biological process that has been investigated. The change of entropy is unidirectional not only on the earth; it is one-way in the flow of energy from the sun to the earth. Not only in this sun, but in the other suns; not only in this galaxy but in other galaxies; not only locally, but in the expansion of the universe, all investigated statistical processes are one-sided.

So what reaction can one have towards a statistical explanation for the observed unidirectionality of radiation and of net entropy change? We cannot rightfully discuss the probability of such a large fluctuation in ordinary statistical terms. What observable meaning does it have to discuss a "statistical collection of universes"? And what "observer" is going to "look" at all those universes and draw statistical conclusions about them? Consider even one universe. Imagine a fluctuation in one region of this universe which is enormous. Let it bring about conditions in which an observer can be present who might "see" such a fluctuation. But how can he "see" the fluctuation, when "seeing" as we understand it implies flow of entropy and energy *from* the object *to* the observer? Not "seeing" the fluctuation, what hope can he have properly to assess the likelihood of such a fluctuation? The difficulties of such an observer lead us to an old question: To what extent is what we observe conditioned by the circumstance that we are here to observe it?

This "selectivity of the observer" brings to mind the current philosophical concerns of Gödel. He argues that philosophy is a subject which is as far behind the times today as physics was in the days of the early Greeks. The key point of his concern is the relation between subject and object. The relevance of such considerations to cosmology can be seen in an argument about *why* the universe has dimensions of several times 10^9 light-years. The following line of reasoning has been suggested by Dicke. To observe the universe requires a mind of a certain degree of intelligence. So far as we know, a brain of this complexity cannot be produced without carbon. Carbon in turn needs for its manufacture thermonuclear reactions in the stars. To carry through the manufacture requires several billion years of stellar evolution. In order to have several billions of years of time available for this manufacture, the universe must be several billions of light-years across. Thus the circumstance that the universe has the size that it does is conditioned by the fact that we are here to observe it!

Whatever one thinks about this line of reasoning, it is of course very different from the older reasoning which related the size of elementary particles to the size of human beings. This argument says that a brain of complexity necessary for the study of elementary particles must contain a large number of elementary neurons and what not. Therefore— one sometimes says—the particle must be small in size relative to the human being who is doing the observing.

Having two very different kinds of arguments that connect the observer with the nature of the physics that he observes, one finds it natural also to ask if the one-sidedness of time originates in the nature of the beings who make the observations.

Next, I would like to discuss the universe as a dynamical system and inquire in what respects it is similar to other dynamical systems and in what respect it is different. In this connection, may I raise a question that has surely troubled many of us: Is the universe a system which has available to it only one quantum state? Is it conceivable that there is not a multitude of possible states which the universe can assume? In order to discuss this topic, we would like to have a model which has no features that are not describable in the form of well-defined equations. Yet at the present time our ability to describe elementary particles is limited. Therefore I would suggest a model in which we "saw off" from the ordinary dynamical description of nature those features we cannot describe very well, and limit the discussion to the dynamics of pure geometry. In the simplest version of general relativity there are no matter fields present; we have the case of empty geometry evolving in time. This is a very limited kind of dynamical system, of course, but it is a very rich dynamical system. In a pure geometry there are, for instance, geons, systems of gravitational radiation held together by their own gravitational attraction, which have very long lives. A geon, although it has not the slightest direct connection with an elementary particle, nevertheless serves as a symbolic reminder that particle phenomena exist! Specifically, we consider an empty, closed space, evolving in time in accordance with Einstein's field equations. We inquire about the dynamical description of such a system. We find it natural to use a point of view familiar in particle mechanics. There we give the coordinate of a particle at one time, and the coordinate of the same particle at a slightly later time. These quantities supply enough information to predict the entire future of the particle. The same kind of dynamical data is equally relevant to a more complicated system, such as the electromagnetic field. There we give the magnetic field throughout space at one time, and the magnetic field throughout space at a slightly later time. Then we have enough information to predict the entire future of the free electromagnetic field. We can even be slightly more general in the way we specify the time at which the magnetic field is to be given. We can specify the magnetic field B' as a function of position on one spacelike hypersurface, σ', and the magnetic field B'' as second function of position on a second spacelike hypersurface, σ''. The hypersurface is described by giving at each point (x, y, z) in space a time coordinate,

$$t' = t'(x, y, z). \tag{1}$$

How much information about the field do we thus require in order to predict the entire future dynamics? We have at each space point one number, the time. At first sight it might appear that we have in addition at each point three numbers, the three field components. However, the magnetic field has zero divergence. Consequently, out of these three numbers per space point, only two are independent. So we must have two field numbers and one time number for each space point, in order to describe the initial configuration of the system. We have ∞^3 space points, so the amount of information we must specify amounts to $(\infty^3)^3$ numbers—on each of the two spacelike hypersurfaces.

When we turn from the dynamics of electromagnetism to the dynamics of space geometry, we might again suppose it reasonable to specify, first, which spacelike hypersurface we are considering, and, then, something about the geometrical conditions on this hypersurface. However, there is one great difference between geometrodynamics and electrodynamics. In electrodynamics the entire space-time manifold is envisaged as prescribed in advance—even if, as usual, it is prescribed to be *flat*. Whether the space is flat or not, one knows what he is doing when he specifies a spacelike hypersurface, or "slice," through this manifold. In geometrodynamics, by contrast, the four-geometry has yet to be found. We do not know what the four-dimensional history is; we cannot say where the three-dimensional spacelike surface cuts through the four-dimensional object. It turns out that it is nevertheless simple to give the requisite data for the dynamics of geometry. One has only to specify two three-dimensional geometries, one for each of two "times." The amount of information given in this way for geometrodynamics corresponds exactly to what one gives in electrodynamics: three numbers per space point on each hypersurface. How one arrives at this number is easy to sketch. To describe a three-dimensional geometry, we customarily give six metric coefficients g_{ik}, as a function of position. But there are three possible coordinate transformations that do not affect the physics. So we have actually six minus three, or three significant numbers per space point to be specified. We have the same amount of information in order to specify the geometry as we have in order to specify the magnetic field. Moreover, when we give this information, then we have told all that there is to be told about time. There is no way and no need to give more. How is it that the specification of three-geometry amounts to a specification of time? It may be worthwhile to outline the basic idea in a little more detail. Symbolically, let $A'B'C'D'E' \cdots$ represent one three-dimensional geometry and $A''B''C''D''E'' \cdots$ represent another. All that is really specified of course is the geometry intrinsic to the spacelike hypersurface; nothing is said about its relation to any other geometry, nor about the distance between one hypersurface and the other.

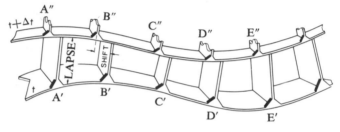

Figure VII-1

To be found from Einstein's field equations are (1) the perpendicular distances from the one hypersurface to the other ("the lapse," $N\Delta t$) and (2) the spacelike displacement or "sideways shift," $N_i\Delta t$, of correspondingly labeled points on the two hypersurfaces—a total of four quantities. We might make a simplified model by taking a thin strip of sheet metal and welding to it perpendicular uprights at the points A', $B' \cdots$. How are we to find out the proper length of each upright and the appropriate place to weld the tip of that upright to the upper strip? As guide in this undertaking we have two important principles: (1) giving everywhere the lapse and shift fixes the four-dimensional geometry intervening between the two specified three-geometries; and (2) this four-geometry must satisfy Einstein's equations. Happily the (00) and (0i) components of those equations give precisely four conditions on the four quantities to be found. In other words, we give the two faces of a sandwich (as especially described by David Sharp in his Princeton A.B. senior thesis) and then Einstein tells us what kind of four-dimensional "meat" is to be inserted between the faces of this sandwich. Moreover, this favorable situation is unchanged by the presence of source terms in the field equations.

A distinction has to be made between the way we have been talking and the way we do the mathematics. We talk of the metrics

$$(ds')^2 = {}^{(3)}g_{ik}{}' \, dx^i \, dx^k$$

and

$$(ds'')^2 = {}^{(3)}g_{ik}{}'' \, dx^i \, dx^k$$

on the two hypersurfaces, and of the difference between them,

$$\Delta^{(3)}g_{ik} = g_{ik}{}'' - g_{ik}{}'.$$

A mathematician would not like the idea of talking about two "nearby hypersurfaces." He prefers to speak of a whole one-parameter continuous family of hypersurfaces, characterized by successive values of a monotonically increasing parameter t. We accede to the use of such a parameter, although we know that no direct physical interest can be attached to the names t and $t + \Delta t$ given to the two hypersurfaces, nor to the separation, Δt, in coordinate time between them. We know too that the separation in proper time, or "lapse," $N\Delta t$, between the two hypersurfaces is what counts, not either factor individually in that expression: neither the nominal time interval Δt nor the correction factor or "lapse function," N. This was acceptable to our mathematical colleague; we go along with him and replace finite differences wherever they appear by derivatives. Thus we can arrange to talk, not about $\Delta^{(3)}g_{ik}$, but about the "time rate of change of three-geometry,"

$$\partial^{(3)}g_{ik}/\partial t.$$

In this way we have a means to reword the original problem. It read previously: Given the three-geometry on each hypersurface, find the four-geometry between them. More specifically, it read: Given ${}^{(3)}g_{ik}{}'$ and ${}^{(3)}g_{ik}{}''$, find the "lapse" and the "shift." Now it has been revised to read: Given ${}^{(3)}g_{ik}(x, y, z, t_0)$ and $[\partial^{(3)}g_{ik}(x, y, z, t)/\partial t]_{t_0}$, find from Einstein's equations the lapse and shift functions $N(x, y, z, t_0)$ and $N_i(x, y, z, t_0)$ in the complete expression for the four-geometry within the sandwich,

$$(ds)^2 = {}^{(3)}g_{ik} \, dx^i \, dx^k + 2N_i \, dx^i \, dt + (N_i N^i - N^2)(dt)^2.$$

The equations for the lapse and shift functions, being field equations, rank as of the second order. An alternative way of describing the situation employs twice as many equations, each of the first order. In formulating these equations insight is gained by introducing the "geometrodynamical field momentum." Even easier in some ways to interpret than this momentum, and yet practically equivalent to it, is the "extrinsic curvature," telling how the three-dimensional hypersurface is curved with respect to the enveloping and yet-to-be-constructed four-geometry. To define this curvature, one constructs unit timelike normals to the hypersurface. A geometrical figure lying in the hypersurface is defined by a set of vertices or by an even larger collection of points. Consider each point to be carried over to a new point separated from the original point by the unit timelike normal at that point. Then the figure is carried over into a new figure in which all distances have been slightly altered. Also all coordinate separations Δx^i have been changed to slightly different separations, $\Delta x^i + \xi^i$. The figure has undergone a strain:

$$\xi^i = K^i{}_j \Delta x^j.$$

The symmetric tensor K_{ij} that measures this strain has been called the tensor of the extrinsic curvature. It has the value

$$K_{ij} = \gamma_{ij}/N,$$

with

$$\gamma_{ik} = \tfrac{1}{2}(\partial^{(3)}g_{ik}/\partial t - N_{i|k} - N_{k|i}).$$

Returning to our picture of uprights connecting one hypersurface with the other, we ask what combination of lapse and shift distinguishes the special four-geometry of the sandwich allowed by Einstein's field equations from all other conceivable four-geometries. The four-geometry that is allowed is special in that it minimizes an expression for action. The action in the case of geometrodynamics, as in the case of electrodynamics, consists of two parts. Of these, one looks like a kinetic energy and the other, like a potential energy. The kinetic term has to do with the amount of the "strain" that takes place in the three-geometry and with the proper time required for the strain to come about. The appropriate measure of the amount of strain turns out to be, according to Arnowitt, Deser, and Misner, the quantity

$$\gamma_2 = (\gamma_i{}^i)^2 - \gamma_i{}^k\gamma_k{}^i$$
$$= (\mathrm{Tr}\,\gamma)^2 - \mathrm{Tr}\,(\gamma^2).$$

The time is measured by the lapse function N. Thus the "kinetic energy" term in the action is γ_2/N^2. The "potential energy" term is $^{(3)}R$, which is the scalar curvature invariant of the three-geometry. The action associated with the sandwich is obtained by adding the "kinetic" term and the "potential" term and integrating over the interior of the sandwich, with the four-volume element

$$(^{(3)}g)^{1/2}\,d^3x\,N\Delta t.$$

Thus the action principle is

$$\Delta t \int (\gamma_2/N + {}^{(3)}RN)(^{(3)}g)^{1/2}\,d^3x = \text{extremum.}$$

Here Δt and the three-geometry and its time rate of change have been given. The problem is to find the remaining features of the four-geometry of the sandwich: the lapse and shift functions, N and N_i. A large value of N means a long lapse of proper time, $N\Delta t$; this means a long, slow change in the geometry, and an almost negligible contribution from the "kinetic" term to the action. In contrast, the "potential" term $^{(3)}R$ contributes more as the sandwich becomes thicker. The action becomes arbitrarily large for an arbitrarily great value of the lapse function, N. No extremum in that direction!

The opposite choice of a small value for the lapse function signifies a thin sandwich, and an almost negligible contribution of the "potential" energy term, $^{(3)}RN$, in the integral. However, the *rate* at which the three-geometry has to accomplish its change becomes in this case very great, and again the action integral can be made arbitrarily large. Between these two extremes of small N and large N we adjust N to minimize the action when we give it the value

$$N = (\gamma_2/^{(3)}R)^{1/2}.$$

The work is not over at this point. We need not only the lapse function but also the three shift functions N_i in order completely to determine the geometry of the sandwich. We find the remaining three functions by extremizing the expression

$$2\Delta t \int ({}^{(3)}R\gamma_2{}^{(3)}g)^{1/2} \, d^3x.$$

In the integrand the shift functions enter only in γ_2, and here only through their covariant derivatives.

   Without going into further detail, we now have the situation laid out in broad outline. Fixing the two "nearby three-geometries" (equivalent to one three-geometry plus its rate of change with respect to an otherwise irrelevant parameter t) gives us a means (rewritten in the form of an action principle) to determine the four-geometry of the thin sandwich. In that way we learn the separation in proper time, $N\Delta t$, between two faces of the thin sandwich. We also have all the information needed to start and to carry through the integration of Einstein's field equations. In other words, nothing now stands in the way of determining the entire four-geometry in which the two faces of the thin sandwich stand immersed. In the end we find out not merely the separation in proper time between the two hypersurfaces, but also (Baierlein and Sharp) their precise location in that entire history of geometry that we name a "space-time manifold." In this sense then, the two three-geometries on the two originally specified spacelike surfaces told all that needed to be told about time. Thus three-geometry, in the context of Einstein's general relativity, may be said to be a "carrier of information about time" in a very beautiful way.

   The fact that information about time is carried by three-geometry means that no other indicator is needed to carry information about time. The Hamilton-Jacobi function S of classical geometrodynamics or the probability amplitude $\psi \sim \exp(iS/h)$ of quantum geometrodynamics does not depend upon three-geometry *and* time, but upon three-geometry alone:

$$S = S({}^{(3)}\mathscr{G})$$
$$\psi = \psi({}^{(3)}\mathscr{G}).$$

The three numbers per space point required to specify a three-geometry in geometrodynamics correspond exactly to the $1+2=3$ numbers required in electrodynamics to specify a hypersurface plus the magnetic field upon this hypersurface. However, in electrodynamics the split of the three numbers into two for dynamics plus one for time is plain for all to see:

$$S = S(t(x, y, z), \; \boldsymbol{B}(x, y, z))$$
$$\psi = \psi(t(x, y, z), \; \boldsymbol{B}(x, y, z)).$$

In geometrodynamics, by contrast, there is no unique way to split off the dynamic information carried by a three-geometry from the information about time carried by the same three-geometry. This impossibility of making a clean cut between information about geometrodynamics and information about time is a consequence of the well-known covariance of general relativity with respect to the many different ways to slice a four-geometry into three-geometries.

BERGMANN

The idea that the three-dimensional geometry determines time holds only with considerable qualifications and is not true locally. Locally we get only differential equations. You make two assumptions. One is that standard boundary conditions must always be imposed at the edge of the three-dimensional domain in which we operate. The second assumption is that the system of highly nonlinear equations that you obtain can in fact be solved in terms of conserved quantities, once you have found those quantities. Neither of these two things has been demonstrated, except by somewhat dubious perturbation methods. I believe that since we do know something about allowable initial value systems involving the g_{ik} and the momenta, or something algebraic which is related to the momenta, and since the relationship between the allowable systems and this one is partially known, we can try to prove these assertions. I am not convinced that these two assertions will eventually be proved to be right.

WHEELER

Analogous issues arise in electromagnetism and can be treated. There the questions of boundary conditions and initial value data are simple. In the case of electromagnetism the analogous "thin sandwich" variational principle is

$$\delta \int (E^2/8\pi - \rho\phi)d^3x = 0$$
$$\boldsymbol{E} = -\partial A/\partial t - \nabla\phi.$$

We give the magnetic field $H = \mathrm{curl}\ A$ on each of two nearby space-like surfaces. In other words, we have given A (up to a gauge transformation) and $\partial A / \partial t$, and we are trying to find out the remaining quantity required to evaluate the electrodynamics throughout the thin sandwich, namely, the electrical scalar potential, ϕ. We have the variational equation to determine ϕ. Granted an appropriate boundary condition, we obtain a unique solution. In the case of gravitation, the situation is analogous. However, instead of having three known potentials A_1, A_2, A_3, we have six known potentials, the metric coefficients g_{ik}. Instead of having one potential ϕ yet to find in order to determine the dynamics within the thin sandwich, we must solve for four potentials, the lapse function N and the shift functions N_1, N_2, N_3—which are equivalent in the information they carry to the still-missing components of the metric, g_{00} and g_{0i}. We have been able to forget the greater part of the machinery of the dynamical formalism, because we are speaking of the action in a thin slice. Out of the familiar $(1/8\pi)\int(E^2 - H^2)d^3x$ we have therefore been able to throw out the H^2 term. We have also been able to throw out the (jA) term here, because both j and A have already been specified; there is nothing to be varied in this term. The only terms that are left to be varied are those which contain the unknown potential: the terms $E^2/8\pi$ and $-\rho\phi$. In a similar way the variational principle of relativity contains many more terms than those we wrote down. We can throw out the missing terms because we are dealing with a thin slice. The missing terms are those which are not affected by variations within the thin sandwich. That is the analogy between the initial-value problems of geometrodynamics and electrodynamics.

What do we do in the electromagnetic case after we have solved the thin-sandwich problem for the potential ϕ? Knowing not only the magnetic potential, but also the electrical scalar potential, we now know not only the magnetic field, but also the electric field. Now we have enough information to predict the entire future of the system. All the dynamics is well determined; but it was not well determined until we solved the initial-value problem. In a similar way, giving in geometrodynamics the two three-dimensional geometries is not enough to permit one at once to start integrating Einstein's field equations. We must first solve the initial-value problem. We must find the four potentials g_{00} and g_{0i} (or N and N_1, N_2, N_3). Only then do we know the field momentum conjugate to the intrinsic geometry; only then do we know the extrinsic curvature; only then do we know all ten potentials; only then do we have the ability to integrate Einstein's equations, or to determine the entire future of the system. Do the four initial-value equations of geometrodynamics permit a unique solution, or a certain limited number of solutions, as the one initial-value equation does in the case of electrodynamics? If so, then we can say that the specification of the two three-geometries provides information about time in the following sense: it determines the four-geometry intervening between these surfaces. This fixed, the entire four-dimensional geometry is uniquely specified. Moreover, the four-geometry determines the proper time interval between the two surfaces. So in this sense three-dimensional geometry is a carrier of information about time.

BERGMANN

The doubts I have do not seem to interfere with the main point of your argument. Whatever may be said about g_{ik} and $\dot{g}_{ik}$, we know that we can get enough information on a three-dimensional surface to have the Cauchy data, namely g_{ik} and the t_k, and then it becomes perhaps a matter of taste whether we insist on your selection of what is definitely known to be legitimate. Is it necessary in the treatment to specify what the Cauchy data ought to be, or is it sufficient to agree that there are some Cauchy data which we must find for each world point so that we can take the problem from there?

WHEELER

Let me translate the question to other terms. We agree that if both the intrinsic geometry and extrinsic geometry of a spacelike hypersurface are given, and if in addition the two are compatible with the four initial-value equations, then we can predict the entire future. Our difference in point of view concerns the appropriate way to go about *finding* compatible initial-value data, that is, an extrinsic curvature compatible with a given intrinsic three-geometry. You suggest that there ought to exist some means of finding compatible initial-value data without your having to be as specific about these means as I am being. I agree. However, I am not interested at the moment in securing greater generality, but only in offering *one* standard method of getting consistent initial-value data which has a long tradition of serviceability in other branches of mathematical physics. The method is simple as applied to geometrodynamics. We write down the three-dimensional variational principle, taking as given the three-dimensional geometry and its time rate of change. We can then find from the initial-value equations consistent values of the N's and the extrinsic curvature which will allow us to predict the future. This is proposed as *a* method which will always give acceptable initial-value data.

Let us look at an example where we can see two three-geometries determining the four-geometry of a thick sandwich and thus the separation in proper time between the two faces of the sandwich. It is difficult to think of a simpler example than that in which each three-geometry has the character of a three-dimensional sphere. We can write the two three-geometries in this form:

$$^{(3)}\mathscr{G}'': \quad a''^2[dX^2 + \sin^2 X(d\theta^2 + \sin^2 \theta \, d\varphi^2)],$$
$$^{(3)}\mathscr{G}': \quad a'^2[dX^2 + \sin^2 X(d\theta^2 + \sin^2 \theta \, d\varphi^2)].$$

What do we find for the lapse function N in this case? If the system has some mass in it, the quantity N, which measures the separation between two spheres, is given by

$$N = \frac{\left(\dfrac{a'' - a'}{x_0'' - x_0'} \right)}{\sqrt{\dfrac{4}{3\pi} \dfrac{M}{a} - 1}}.$$

From this expression we find the interval of proper time required for the dynamics to carry space from the one three-geometry to the other with this result:

$$\text{proper time} = N(x_0'' - x_0').$$

The mass may be in the form of dust, or in the form of geons, or in some other form, distributed uniformly throughout space. The main point is that the separation in proper time between one hypersurface and the other is completely specified in this way. This is an elementary example of how giving two three-dimensional geometries fixes time.

There is another general point to be made in this connection. Suppose we construct for our problem with its ideal spherical symmetry an energy relation comprising rest energy, kinetic energy, and gravitational energy,

$$M + M\left(\frac{da}{dt}\right)^2 - \frac{4}{3\pi}\frac{GM^2}{a} = 0.$$

This well-known conserved quantity, however, differs in a remarkable way from the corresponding energy integral of more familiar dynamical problems. The energy in such problems can have any value one may choose to assign to it. Here, however, the conserved quantity necessarily has the value zero. The geometrodynamical system has a smaller number of degrees of freedom than one would otherwise have thought reasonable for this mechanical system. In other words, the universe is not a system for which we can use the concept of energy. The vanishing of our expression for an energylike quantity is one way of expressing this fact.

The energy is definable for a system which is asymptotically flat, but is not definable for a system which is closed. This follows most obviously from the fact that in the latter case there is no asymptotically flat space in which we can get far enough away from the system in order to measure its gravitational pull. Just as we cannot define energy for a closed universe, so it makes no sense to define angular momentum for a closed universe. There is no asymptotically flat space with respect to which we can define angular momentum.

We can consider the quantum theory of a closed system described by Einstein's equations. Having no possibility of using a concept of energy or angular momentum in a closed universe, we have no means of giving the familiar quantum numbers of energy and angular momentum which specify the difference between one quantum state and another. This circumstance suggests that there may be *no* quantum numbers available for describing the states of a closed system. In other words, one is naturally led to consider the hypothesis that there is a *unique quantum state* for a closed universe. I do not yet see any easy way to test this hypothesis, nor how to find out whether this hypothesis follows as a consequence of the equations.

What consequences follow from the hypothesis that the universe has only one accessible quantum state: no first integrals, no energy, and no angular momentum? The simplest examples of solvable problems of dynamics in relativity describe systems which characteristically go through a phase of expansion, reach a maximum dimension, and then shrink in size. One case in which the dynamics can be carried out in detail is the so-called Taub universe. This is a model universe in which all the effective energy of the system is derived from pure gravitational radiation. It is a solution in which there is no matter present and no electromagnetic fields. The space is curved up into closure by the effective density of energy of gravitational waves alone. To visualize the model, start with a spherical universe, and fit into this three-sphere the standing gravitational wave which has the longest wavelength compatible with the dimensions of the three-sphere. This is the only mode of radiation that we excite. We impart to this mode a certain critical amplitude such that the effective energy of the wave will be just enough to curve up the universe into the already postulated closure. This Taub universe follows a behavior very much like that of a model universe in which there is "real" matter present.

There is no cosmological term in the equations. The Taub universe is homogeneous. Every point is like every other point. However, the model is not isotropic. The space is curved more in one direction than another, by reason of the gravitational wave superimposed on a space that is already curved. The extra curvature produced by the gravitational wave in an otherwise perfectly curved, spherical space is not very great. At the moment of maximum expansion, the wave produces, say, up to 20 per cent variation of curvature in one direction compared to that in the other. But as the universe contracts, the gravitational wave gets stronger, and the curvature increases in one direction compared to that in the other. In this contracting phase of the Taub universe, there comes a moment when the effective region of space available for motion becomes very small, and world lines of particles become snarled in a very puzzling way. What happens next? Obviously this state of affairs is not easily discussed in terms of classical theory.

It once appeared tempting to argue that we always arrive at a state of infinite curvature if we follow the dynamics of the closed universe far enough. Only one way out of the impasse suggested itself. Consider the analogy between (1) a universe undergoing a succession of expansions from an almost singular state and recontractions to such a state and (2) a billiard ball rolling about on a billiard table with sides having an incommensurable length ratio. The "bounce" of the universe from its almost singular state is to be compared with the bounce of the ball from the side of the billiard table. Start out the billiard ball on the table with a well-defined energy and definite angular momentum with respect to some chosen origin. Then the ball strikes the side. The collision changes the angular momentum. Eventually the ball executes quasi-ergodic motion inside this enclosure. Each path of rectilinear motion of the ball can be compared to a phase of expansion or contraction of the universe. Each reflection of the ball by the side can be compared with a stage of high compression in which quantum effects must be considered in order to treat the next phase of the system. This is a system in which one of the usual first integrals of the motion has disappeared. The motion is quasi-ergodic in the sense that in the course of time the ball runs arbitrarily close to every point on the table. Of course the billiard ball is not absolutely quasi-ergodic; it is not completely free of constants of the motion, because in this problem we know that energy has meaning and is conserved. In this respect there is not a full correspondence between the mechanical system and the geometrodynamical system. Apart from the fact that we have an energy integral for the billiard ball, and not for the universe, it would have been tempting to use the analogy that the universe is a system which, because of its quasi-ergodic character, can be in a single quantum state and yet can manifest all the richness of every possible motion. This concept of a single "quasi-ergodic" quantum state for a closed universe may still be productive to explore. However, there is a recent development in relativity theory that appears pertinent to the discussion. Misner has shown that the Taub universe is indistinguishable from the NUT (Newman-Unti-Tamburino) universe. It turns out that the Taub universe changes uniformly from closed to open without ever developing infinite curvature! It changes from a closed universe to an open universe along a null hypersurface. The open model and the closed model are smooth continuations of each other.

How does one deal with this strange mixture of open universe and closed universe? The context in which one discusses this topic is entirely classical—as it is also a purely classical context in which one comes up against the development of infinite curvature in finite proper time. One is free to believe that neither the singularities nor the transition from closed to open have any place in the proper quantum mechanical analysis of geometrodynamics. It is especially inviting to try this view because the Schrödinger formulation of quantum geometrodynamics deals exclusively with three-dimensional geometries $^{(3)}\mathscr{G}$ that are both spacelike and free of singularity.

The Schrödinger state function appears as a function of the three-geometry, so:

$$\psi = \psi(^{(3)}\mathscr{G}).$$

The following line of reasoning may show how this treatment of quantum geometrodynamics is connected with the standard Schrödinger mechanics of a nonrelativistic particle. In classical theory the dynamics of a particle is specified by giving the coordinate at two times. The state function of the particle in quantum theory depends on the coordinate at one time. Likewise in electromagnetic theory the classical dynamics is specified by giving the magnetic field at two times, but the quantum mechanical state function depends upon the magnetic field on one hypersurface. Similarly, the classical dynamics of space is specified by giving the three-geometry on two hypersurfaces, but the Schrödinger probability amplitude depends upon the three-geometry on only one spacelike hypersurface. In other words, the state function gives the probability of a particular three-geometry. If it is said that in quantum theory there is no sense in talking of anything but *closed* spacelike hypersurfaces, then we have no possibility of passing over from the closed Taub universe to the open NUT universe. We just cannot get outside of this system of closed spacelike surfaces. In such a quantum context it does not seem out of place to think of a closed universe as something like a quasi-ergodic system which passes over from one cycle of expansion and recontraction to another cycle of expansion and re-contraction—of perhaps very different maximum volume—when it approaches what in classical theory would be a singular state of maximum contraction.

Our picture of the universe as a quasi-ergodic system, which can be in only one acceptable quantum state, is a working hypothesis which might have value in the discussion of the issues that now face us. First, this picture suggests that the universe is a dynamical system completely different from any kind of dynamical system which we have ever discussed before. Second, the picture indicates that the universe is not a system that we can observe from outside; the observer is a part of what he observes. Observation under these conditions presents new features; Everett's so-called "relative state formulation" of quantum mechanics does provide one self-consistent way of describing such situations. Although we are very far from having seen our way through these problems, there is a well-defined formalism in which to carry out the analysis.

X

The idea that the universe might be an enormous fluctuation seems absurd, and I would like to argue from observations that this idea is wrong. Assume that we make observations as usual in the theory. Using a sort of "Bayes' theorem," we have *a priori* theory A and theory B, and then make observations. As a result, let us say, the observations tend to increase the probability against theory B relative to A.

Suppose we speak about the probability of theories of the universe, the probability that the universe started from an equal *a priori* probability, or that it started from some special condition. In the way that we ordinarily decide theories through observations, the observations always weight the probabilities in the same sense. This is not really defensible.

Let us begin with a hypothesis which statistical-mechanics books sometimes begin with: "All states are *a priori* equally probable in phase space." Suppose also that we would like to argue that this rule is against observation. To do this, we start with the following two *a priori* theories. Either with a probability of .99999 all states are equally likely (and notice that the .99999 is distributed over all those states equally), or with a probability of 10^{-100} the universe had in the beginning some special state that can be defined in less than 150 million words. This means that a few especially allowed states are different from all the other states. If we suppose that the universe is a fluctuation, then we can use the analogy of black and white balls in a box that has been shaken forever. If we look and find all the black balls on one side and the white ones on the other, then we can say that they got there by a fluctuation. But suppose that we look at only a part of the box and find that all the black balls are on one side of this region and all the white balls are on the other. It has been fluctuating for all time. We can then ask what is the most likely condition to be found in a region at which we have not yet looked. From the equal *a priori* probability hypothesis the remaining region is more likely to be uniform. We must take the minimum fluctuation, consistent with what has already been observed, to be the most likely if equal probabilities are assumed. Assuming that we observe a subsystem which is sufficiently large that fluctuation is unlikely, then the other possible interpretation of our observation of the black balls separated from the white ones is that they were arranged initially in an easily describable way. In an initial description containing 150 million words, the balls were, say, all on one side, and what we see now is a remnant of this. Then we expect that this remnant will be similar to the other parts.

So we have two theories, one which predicts that if we look in places where we have not looked before, the balls will be mixed up. The other theory predicts that they would with a small probability be correlated in phase from the past. This can be checked observationally. Every time a man looks in the dirt and finds a bone that is like a fossil he saw before, we have more evidence that the world did come from an origin, and that there was an evolution of the animals rather than a fluctuation which put things in that condition. Since we perpetually make the observations and look at things we did not see before, we can take the view that we perpetually increase the odds for the hypothesis that the universe in the past was somewhat out of the ordinary. This produces the direction in time from observations. This result is connected with the condition that in the past the world was more organized, or thermodynamically correlated in phase space, than it is today. I think that is the result of observation and that the statistical fluctuation theory can be eliminated as an allowable hypothesis.

However, according to the equal *a priori* probability hypothesis, it is likely that the world was created by fluctuation. In order to create people and fossils, and so on, by evolution, the sun must have been shining all this time, there must have been this enormous one-sidedness of entropy. Calculating according to the present theory of precisely equal *a priori* probability for all states, it does turn out that the odds are against evolution, and for the fluctuation.

MORRISON

That is right; the sun is so inefficient. Since entropy actually does increase if you turn it around and run it backwards, it must be more probable that the world was produced by a fluctuation.

GRÜNBAUM

Von Weizsäcker in a paper called "The Second Law of Thermo-dynamics and the Distinction between the Past and Future," in the *Annalen der Physik* of 1939, made just this point.

GOLD

Let me add my absurd story, which is in the same vein. This is the argument that the world will end tomorrow. Biology is obviously something extremely improbable. The probability that complicated structures do not exist seems to be enormous. Now we think of the analogous situation in which we find some extremely unlikely event, such as monkeys typing out Shakespeare correctly, page after page. If we know that the monkeys are bashing it out without any sense, then the chance against the succeeding letter being the right one is twenty-six to one. At every stage we would say, "The next step that is going to happen is of course going to be the wrong one." So if biology were a succession of enormous improbabilities we would be here only because so far it has gone right; but that does not diminish the high probability that the next step will be wrong.

BERGMANN

I think that in this whole discussion, we are using the term "prob-ability" in a very loose and perhaps indefensible fashion. At least I cannot attach any real significance to it, and it is likely that the so-called hypothesis of equal *a priori* probability is logically inconsistent to begin with.

X

I am subject to that criticism. I have never found myself able to use the concept of probability except in an inconsistent, indefensible way.

BERGMANN

Suppose that we construct a phase space for the whole universe, although I strongly doubt that this can be done, and then that we re-quire all points of this phase space to be as probable as all other points. There is only one universe, so there must be only one point, and this universe is presumably as probable as any other universe.

MORRISON

But the question of probabilities for the whole universe need not arise. X is speaking about large finite volumes of space. The cosmological problem centers on what happens when we add to this volume.

X

Yes. That is one possibility, but even if we want to talk in terms of the whole universe, we can do it. Suppose we want to decide on a theory about the initial state of the universe. It is true that the universe starts from one state in the classical view. We do not know what that state is. When we do not know something, we have the theory of probability, indefensible as it is, to help us find the odds between the different states. So we must start out with an *a priori* hypothesis as to which state the universe may be in, before we make observations. Some people propose that in order to describe the universe, its possible states must be equally likely before any observations are made. I say that this will lead to trouble, and that we should start out with the following: all states that take too many words to describe are equally likely, but there is however a very small probability, say, 10^{-150}, but not $10^{-10^{10}}$, that any state which can be described in a million words is also equally likely. So we have given a little extra weight to some special state. Now we observe the universe and use the Bayes' theorem backwards. After making the observation, we calculate, according to our hypothesis for weighting the states, the odds that the universe looks as it does. So in this view, for all states that are not simply describable in words, the most likely one is that in which the rest of the world is "smeared out," even if the part we observe is fluctuating. When we observe regions that have order in them, we increase the weight *a posteriori* on the special states. Ultimately, we come to the conclusion that the universe started in some kind of special state, one that can be described in a few words. We understand our world by saying it started from some kind of special low-entropy state that has been evolving toward more chaos since. I do not think that this line is completely indefensible.

VIII. The Strong Cosmological Principle, Indeterminacy, and the Direction of Time

D. LAYZER

Summary

The strong cosmological principle asserts that a *complete* description of the universe does not distinguish between different positions or directions in space at a given instant of cosmic time. It therefore implies that a complete description of the universe has a statistical character, a conclusion that seems at first sight to be inconsistent with the apparently unlimited possibilities for acquiring detailed information about the universe through observation. A careful examination of this question discloses, however, that, in a certain well-defined sense, microscopic information is actually not present in a universe satisfying the strong cosmological principle. A complete set of ideal observations would just suffice to fix all the parameters that figure in a complete statistical description. If the universe is spatially infinite, any two realizations of the same statistical description are observationally and mathematically indistinguishable. If it is spatially finite, distinguishable realizations exist. But if one regards the time axis as a closed loop of finite extent, the multiplicity of distinguishable representations has no physical significance; the various realizations are not ordered in time, but coexist as members of a Gibbs ensemble.

The kind of indeterminacy considered here is basically different from, though of course compatible with, that introduced by quantum mechanics. It does not affect the accuracy with which any physical quantity can be measured. Instead it introduces an asymmetry between the two directions of time. The strong cosmological principle, together with an assumption concerning the uniqueness of the universe, implies that a mathematical description of the universe can unfold in a single time direction only, the direction that corresponds to an initial cosmic expansion. The future is then uniquely characterized by its predictability, the past by the fact that its traces are contained in the present state of the universe. The irreversibility of such macroscopic processes as heat conduction in nearly isolated systems derives ultimately from the absence of microscopic information about the initial state, and hence all subsequent states, of the universe, which implies that, except in specially contrived situations, microscopic information about the initial state of a nearly isolated system is nonexistent. The macroscopic transport equations, which are time-asymmetrical, then follow from the time-symmetrical microscopic equations.

111

It is generally agreed that irreversibility in macroscopic systems has its origin in the asymmetry of the initial or boundary conditions that are normally imposed on them. This asymmetry has a statistical character. The irreversibility of transport phenomena, for example, depends on the irrelevance of microscopic information about initial states. Thus, in heat conduction a knowledge of the initial temperature distribution suffices for a prediction of the temperature distribution at all later times. But if microscopic information is unnecessary for the prediction of future macrostates, it must be necessary for the prediction of past macrostates. In this way the postulate of microscopic irrelevance singles out a direction in time.

The modern notion of entropy as a measure of uncertainty enables one to formulate the assumption of microscopic irrelevance in precise mathematical terms. The difficulty lies in understanding where the uncertainty about initial states comes from. That a detailed microscopic description of a physical system comes closer to reality than a statistical description seems almost self-evident. But it is hard to reconcile this intuition with the postulate of microscopic irrelevance. One might, perhaps, be tempted to regard irreversibility as being contingent on the macroscopic viewpoint. But the problem of accounting for the asymmetric character of macroscopic initial and boundary conditions would still remain.

I wish to suggest that a natural solution to the problem emerges from considerations of the space-time structure of the universe as a whole.

Such an approach may at first sight seem unnecessarily speculative. But the problem of understanding why certain kinds of boundary and initial conditions are appropriate in macroscopic physics is essentially one of understanding how macroscopic systems are related to the rest of the universe. Cosmology seems to offer a more adequate framework for a discussion of this question than macroscopic physics.

In the present context cosmology must be understood in a broader sense than the usual one, for it is essential to consider not only the large-scale structure of the universe but the local irregularities as well. The behavior of a universe without irregularities is completely reversible. Relativistic models that expand indefinitely from a state of maximum density may equally well be thought of as contracting from a state of infinite dispersion; oscillating models, of course, are invariant under time reversal. As for the steady-state universe, time reversal converts it into a contracting universe with continuous annihilation of matter—a process that would seem to be as acceptable as continuous creation. If, then, irreversibility is a property of the universe as a whole, it must be intimately related to the existence of local irregularities. What considerations can we rely on for guidance in constructing a realistic nonuniform model of the universe?

It is often said that the universe is unique. As applied to the actual universe, this statement is a truism; but as applied to the class of conceivable model universes, it has considerable heuristic value. Used in this way, it is not a new principle peculiar to cosmology but merely an application of the usual criterion of economy or simplicity; it directs us toward the simplest cosmological postulates whose consequences are in accord with observation.

Cosmology in the restricted sense is based on the postulate of spatial uniformity and isotropy—the so-called cosmological principle. As applied to a universe with local irregularities, the cosmological principle states that neither the mean density field nor the mean velocity field at a given instant of cosmic time serves to define a preferred position or direction in space. The obvious generalization of this postulate is a statement that I shall call the strong cosmological principle: Every spatial section of the universe is statistically homogeneous and isotropic. By this I mean that any complete mathematical description of the universe is invariant under spatial translation and rotation, so that at any given instant of cosmic time there are no preferred positions or directions in space.

The mathematical properties of statistically homogeneous and isotropic distributions are familiar from the theory of turbulence. However, the strong cosmological principle has a basically different meaning from the assumption of statistical homogeneity and isotropy in turbulence theory.

When we describe the state of a bounded system in statistical terms, we ignore a large quantity of detailed information about the system, because it is inaccessible or uninteresting or both. Nevertheless, we regard the detailed information as meaningful and potentially relevant. We could, for example, make detailed predictions about a particular realization of a turbulent flow if we knew enough about the initial and boundary conditions. The situation is fundamentally different in an unbounded distribution characterized by statistical homogeneity and isotropy.

Let us first consider the case of an infinite universe satisfying the strong cosmological principle. It can be shown that a statistical description specifies the microscopic state of such a universe as closely as it can be specified. Conversely, the average properties of such a universe—"average" being used here to mean a spatial average—completely determine all the statistical quantities—joint probability distributions, moments, and so on—that figure in the statistical description. In short, an infinite, statistically homogeneous and isotropic universe *contains no microscopic information.*

As the simplest example of such a universe, consider a Poisson distribution of mass points in Euclidean space. This distribution is characterized by a single number, the mathematical expectation of the number density of points in a cell of arbitrary volume. Because the distribution is ergodic, this expectation can be approximated arbitrarily closely by a spatial average extended over a sufficiently large region of space. Now suppose that we try to compare two realizations of the same Poisson distribution. Let us focus attention on a particular finite volume in the first realization. Dividing this volume into cells, we may characterize the distribution of mass points within it by a set of occupation numbers. No matter how large the volume or how small the cells, the probability associated with this set of occupation numbers is, of course, finite. Hence it must be possible to find in the second realization a volume—in fact infinitely many volumes—in which the distribution of mass points reproduces the distribution in the first region to any given degree of precision. It follows that the two realizations are indistinguishable.

Essentially the same argument applies to any statistically homogeneous and isotropic distribution of infinite extent.

The argument applies also to finite, oscillating, model universes, provided that we regard the time axis as a closed loop. The statistical description specifies a complete ensemble of finite realizations, all of which are on exactly the same footing.

If the preceding considerations are correct, the strong cosmological principle can account in a general way for the irrelevance of microscopic information in certain macroscopic contexts. But of course microscopic information is not *always* irrelevant. We are therefore obliged to consider how situations in which it *is* irrelevant actually arise. This leads directly to the problem of the formation of astronomical systems. Fortunately, we are here concerned only with a few broad aspects of this problem, which may be amenable to more or less rigorous investigation. Although such an investigation has been begun, it is still in a preliminary stage [Layzer, 1963]. Nevertheless, a brief account of the lines along which it is proceeding may illuminate the present discussion.

Near the beginning of the expansion, when, as I shall assume, the density of matter was extremely high, the distribution of matter must have been much simpler than it is now. If we go sufficiently far back in time, we may even find that only a small number of free parameters—or perhaps none at all—is needed to specify the state of the universe completely. It is conceivable, for example, that the state of maximum compression is unique, being determined entirely by physical laws. Suppose that we take some sufficiently simple early state of the universe as our starting point. Can we then infer from the laws of physics how local irregularities will subsequently form and develop, and thereby predict the highly complex distribution of matter and motion we observe today? I have tried to show that the gradual development of local irregularities, leading ultimately to the formation of a hierarchy of self-gravitating systems, results from gravitational interactions in an expanding medium, after electromagnetic processes in an early stage of the expansion have caused the energy per unit mass associated with the local structure to assume its present (negative) value. For the purpose of the present discussion, then, let us assume that one can arrive at a statistical description of the present-day universe by tracing its development from an earlier state characterized by a small number of parameters. We have already concluded that the description, in spite of its statistical character, is complete. What implications does this picture of the universe and its evolution have for the nature of time?

Although our only assumption concerns the spatial structure of the universe, our picture does exhibit a clear asymmetry between the two directions of time, because the spatial structure automatically causes the postulate of microscopic irrelevance to be satisfied. Since the universe is at the same time a single realization and a complete ensemble of realizations, its microscopic properties are entirely determined by statistical laws. It follows that a mathematical description of the universe can "unfold" in one direction only; by definition, this is the direction of the future. Thus the future is uniquely characterized by its predictability. On the other hand, the present state contains traces of the past only, not of the future. Thus memory pertains uniquely to the past.

These features of the temporal structure of the universe have obvious correlates in our subjective experience of time. We remember the past but not the future; we can predict the future but not the past; without records, the historian's task would be impossible. Finally, the awareness of succession—the feeling of time gradually unfolding (though not always at the same rate)—corresponds to the way in which the mathematical description unfolds; in the description, as in the reality, one must traverse the past in order to reach the future. In these matters, as with other aspects of perception and awareness, the structure of subjective experience seems to correspond in a more or less simple way to the structure of our mathematical description of what is being experienced.

WHEELER

For the sake of clarity, I should say that the concept of a single quantum state of the universe is really rather different from the idea that there is a unique state of maximum condensation for an oscillating universe. The concept I was speaking about was one of an ergodic universe which undergoes a different kind of bounce each time. It bounces, so to speak, in accordance with a kind of probability factor governing the chances about how a cycle is related to the one preceding it. No other essential information is given. This is a very loose way of talking about something that should be treated as a quantum-mechanical system. I do not know how to improve on this treatment. I would not think of a unique state of maximum condensation, nor even of a unique macrostate.

MORRISON

Would you then in some sense envision that there is a predictability, in the sense of an expectation value of any operator, but not that the realization of any given development in a system should come from a single measurement?

WHEELER

I do not even know how to talk sensibly about this question because I do not know how to describe the measurement of this system. It has to be measured from the inside. One cannot form a wave pattern if he is talking about a system that is built out of one quantum state. This is a question for the "relative state formulation" type of description. There is a significant difference in interpretation.

HARWIT

The problem Layzer described looks very much like what Lifshitz did. He started out with a homogeneous, isotropic universe which is quite arbitrary, except that he set the cosmological constant equal to zero. Then, for all linear types of interaction, he traced the evolution of general, growing tensorial perturbations. Unless some nonlinearity is introduced which will complicate the theory, I do not see how this description would differ from the one you suggest in which the initial state is a superposition of different harmonics, which then evolve at calculable rates. What are the differences between your treatment and Lifshitz'?

LAYZER

Lifshitz studied the rate of growth of linear disturbances and showed that in fact some grew and others decayed, but that if one relied on statistical fluctuations to provide the initial irregularities, they would not grow large enough in the available time to account for the existence of galaxies. My approach proceeds from a consideration of the energy associated with local irregularities and of the spectral distribution of this energy. At present the local irregularities—chiefly galaxies and galaxy clusters—have a mean binding energy per unit mass of about 10^{14} erg/gm. It can be shown that as we look backward in time this number will remain approximately constant as long as gravitational forces dominate the motions of particles. On the other hand, the amplitude of the density fluctuations will diminish as we look farther and farther back in time. Specifically, the binding energy per unit mass is proportional to the product $\alpha^2 G \bar{\rho} \lambda^2$, where α is the r.m.s. fractional density fluctuation, G is Newton's constant, $\bar{\rho}$ is the mean density, and λ is the density-autocorrelation distance. This formula, by the way, is not restricted to small values of α. As the universe expands, $\bar{\rho}$ varies as S^{-3} and λ increases no faster than S, where S is the cosmic scale factor. Hence α^2 increases at least as fast as S. The upshot of this argument is that enough binding energy to account for the existence of galaxies and other astronomical systems can be stored in very inconspicuous density fluctuations at a sufficiently early stage of the cosmic expansion.

But these initial density fluctuations, while inconspicuous, are nevertheless very much greater than the random fluctuations considered by Lifshitz. How do they arise? Again we may profitably consider the energetic aspects of the problem. I mentioned that the binding energy per unit mass was approximately conserved as long as gravitational forces dominated the motions of particles. At a sufficiently early stage in the cosmic expansion, when the mean density is comparable to atomic density, matter will be fully ionized and, if large-scale density fluctuations have not yet come into being, Coulomb forces will greatly overshadow the gravitational forces. You will recall that the electrostatic interaction between a proton and an electron is 10^{39} times as great as the gravitational interaction. In these circumstances it can be shown that the mean energy per unit mass associated with local irregularities is not conserved but decreases. Rough estimates indicate that Coulomb interactions at this stage of the expansion *could* produce a negative mean energy of the required magnitude, but more detailed calculations are needed to decide whether this will actually happen. Such calculations are now in progress. The temperature is assumed to be zero initially, and the effects of nuclear reactions, Coulomb interactions, and radiation are all taken into account.

To sum up, Lifshitz' treatment and mine are mutually compatible, but they focus on different aspects of the problem. The apparent contradiction between Lifshitz' result and mine vanishes when one recognizes that the initial conditions contemplated in the two treatments are very different and that in my treatment nongravitational forces play an essential part in shaping the energy spectrum associated with local irregularities at an early stage of the cosmic expansion.

GOLD

Your question about information is the famous geneticist's problem. Either the information content required to construct a human is entirely in the genes, or else the information content of the genes is much less than the required amount. The question is essentially about how the information should be defined. It is not clear to me whether we should define the quantity of information in such a way that it appears to grow spontaneously, or whether we should define it so that the content of information is conserved.

MORRISON

That is exactly what I would have said. This question is the same as that of whether the number π contains infinite or a relatively small amount of information. I think that Layzer's view must be that it contains an infinite amount, and of course there is a certain plausibility to that. But this view also implies that the initial stage or quantum state of energy should be calculable without error. Any error would be enormously magnified. This question about information is the central issue.

BONDI

It seems to me that in any scientific work we must agree to disregard certain things. We must disregard certain features of experiments in order to undertake a formal treatment. If we had to give full details of any phenomenon in the classical picture, certainly we could never predict anything at all.

We can apply this principle of relevance to the significant sub-systems of universe only if there is an infinity of them, either because the universe is infinite in space or because it is infinite in time either through being in a steady state or being an oscillating universe. With a single circle of growth, we would be very much limited in applying this principle. I think this is the way to get around the problem of uniqueness. What I am saying probably is essentially equivalent to Layzer's point of view, but unless we make some such assumption about this, then we are caught in the uniqueness complex, which means essentially that things are unpredictable.

LAYZER

The behavior of the universe can be both unique and predictable if we admit the kind of indeterminacy discussed in my paper—that is, if we regard a certain kind of microscopic information about the universe as unspecified beforehand. As far as I can see, this point of view does not bring us into conflict with experiment. We can, of course, acquire microscopic information of the kind I say is not specified beforehand, but we need to expend negative entropy to do it. That is, we must in a sense supply the required information ourselves. If we do not actually do this, then, I suggest, no significance can be attached to the statement that, say, a particular atom is at a particular place in space and time and not at some other place.

MORRISON

What do you mean by saying that no significance is ever attached to such a statement? Do you mean simply that some things cannot be predictable on this basis, and that these things are therefore irrelevant? If you give any independent criteria of significance, things might satisfy it, but it is only internal information that you set in advance.

LAYZER

By significant information I mean information that ought to figure in a complete description of the universe. Conversely, I would regard as insignificant any information whose existence had no observable consequences.

IX. The Instability of the Future[1]

P. MORRISON

I think of my remarks as being very conservative and somewhat iconoclastic. They are conservative in the sense that what I say is not particularly new, but follows from the work of Poincaré and of Gibbs, and they are iconoclastic since they tend to assert the supremacy of the thermodynamics box. I think that we can draw the following diagram of logical dependence.

$$RAD \longleftarrow TH \longrightarrow COS$$

The symmetrical differential equations give the connection between thermodynamics and the radiative arrow of time. I think of course that thermodynamics determines the cosmological arrow of time. However, there always exists also a weak but determining connection from cosmology to thermodynamics. I am going to argue that there are cosmological features upon which depends more or less everything that thermodynamics can say. But these features are very general ones. They correspond to a restraint upon cosmologies which is so weak that they amount to saying nothing very important about cosmologies. I am going to try to deny that any specific feature from the cosmological side, such as contraction or expansion, has any important consequence on the thermodynamics.

Let me just make an aside which throws some light by metaphor on my view. Consider engineering procedures for making an unusual film. How could we make a film in which, say, a hen becomes smaller and dwindles to a pullet, then to a chick, and then crawls back into the pieces of a shell which reassembles itself into an egg? Now, it is perhaps only an engineering difficulty that prevents us from feeding this animal with food whose phase space is so correlated that it in fact does this!

121

Most people would say that this film was run backwards. However, I undertake to make this film in a different way. In this movie I will have a clock which I swear is honest, and which runs forwards in real time, and at the right scale. In every frame the viewer will see that clock, but he will not see what is in between the frames; that is another story.

I grow ten thousand eggs in an incubator from a genetically pure set of hen genes. The first frame I take shows the oldest hen, the second frame shows a hen which was born a little after that, and so on down to the hatching egg. Without very much difficulty I produce statistically a film that simulates to any degree of accuracy the backward running of time. Now a clever critic would look at the last part of the film showing the egg shell fitting together. He would notice that the cracks are blurred, and would say that there is something strange about that. But with an additional budget, I can guarantee to make that look all right, to any degree of accuracy.

BONDI

Of course the whole thing depends on the theorem of the indistinguishability of all hens.

MORRISON

Exactly. It depends precisely on that theorem. But this discussion is meant to show that while it is not very hard to tell physicists apart, it is harder to tell hens apart, and it is very difficult to tell electrons apart. Still, this difficulty is a purely technical matter. A sufficient expenditure of free energy will enable me to do the job, within any degree of noise that you are willing to allow me. So running the film backward is a kind of partial information. I believe that the incompleteness of information is a major feature of all descriptions of the world. Unless we begin with a decision on this thesis of whether knowledge is partial or complete, we cannot find, I think, a unique answer to the questions we have been discussing.

I would say that we have a dichotomy. I can easily believe that theories exist in which an additional feature must be introduced to give rise to any anisotropy of time, if such theories are in some sense analytic or pseudoanalytic theories. Theories of this type admit of Wheeler's initial-value problem, in which there are a pair of surfaces for which everything is known. I agree that if a cosmology includes such circumstances in which everything is known from the beginning, then whether a film of it is being run forwards or backwards may depend on some quite new assumption, or some special features of the theory. These theories I cannot discuss. I really do not believe that such theories exist, but if they do exist they certainly have their own problems and they do not belong in the same category. But in any theory in which the description of the world includes the sense of partial knowledge of systems, strictly thermodynamical criteria are adequate to define the arrow of time's anisotropy.

I would like to describe "partial knowledge" in a way that removes any flavor of subjectivity that this term may appear to have. The issue about partial knowledge could be considered more objectively as a question about the existence of independent world lines. "Independent" means "possessing some feature not described in a prestated, completely defined form." I would say that in cosmology this probably, but not certainly, implies that given the absence of a completely analytical theory, the only thing else required is the existence of at least weak coupling between any subsystem and a larger system. These things seem very hard to deny in the context.

These three views—the subjective one of partial knowledge, the objective one of independent world lines or causal chains, and the one of the imperfectly isolated system—are not all quite equivalent. A special kind of postulate would be necessary in order to make them equivalent. Such a postulate would be like that of "sufficient reason." This can be put another way. Unless formal predictions of a mathematical theory infer precisely what is going to happen, we cannot expect that specific correlations will arise between the coordinates and the decimal expansion of π. That is the kind of theorem I want to state: among the numbers in the decimal expansion of π, there do not occur very many which represent the coordinates of a particular event that is about to occur next. The number π, or any other transcendental number, is a generator of a pseudorandom sequence. It is in no sense really random. It is really completely fixed. There can be no doubt that in the expansion of π the coordinates of every event occur, but can we always associate the numbers with the events? I deny that a theory can be found which maps a transcendental number onto the events in the world. If this can be done, then I must agree that additional investigation of this new theory is necessary to find the reason for the anisotropy of time. If, however, we do not insist upon the existence of such a theory, then the thermodynamics will explain the time anisotropy.

We consider the picture of Liouville dynamics, classical dynamics of an isolated system, where a Hamiltonian can be defined. There is a Poincaré recurrence time. This recurrence time is very long; it remains very long even if the measurements are coarse-grained. If there is recurrence, and if we wish to study the system for a length of time which is comparable to the recurrence time, then we do not have to be concerned about the arrow of time in this system. It is quite unlikely that such systems could be formed in any cosmology, and even if they could be, they would not remain isolated during the entire Poincaré recurrence time. No assumption of dynamics will guarantee this result, of course. Once we say this, we have removed a great number of the problems in the elaboration of the theory. We should be able to recognize the relation of this to the ensembles of Gibbs. This is not a probabilistic statement; it is a statement about coupling. The probabilistic statement comes next.

Imagine a machine which contains a tape in which π is expanded. This machine behaves irreversibly; it is an engine. It must of course have a source of free energy. The machine can work in all kinds of ways. It can work by the difference in concentration of radiation; it can work in the presence of a piece of iron whose gravitational energy alone is enough to run it; it can work with any chemical other than iron, and so on. It has a very wide number of possibilities to work on. The machine works for a very long time because it is very neatly made with only the slightest degree of energy loss. It has an output consisting of position and velocity of a rod which moves back and forth symmetrically, say in a Lorentzian curve.

The machine is a box with a rod, a tape, and an energy source. This is the only place at which the cosmology enters. For example, a cosmology may deny the possibility of making such a thing at an arbitrary stage of development. But I think that this connection with cosmology is so minimal that we have only a very slight constraint upon the type of cosmology which is compatible with this treatment.

The output of the machine is then a symmetrical motion, except for a slight decline of energy of the whole system. Now, suppose that the machine runs through the digits of π skipping in some way which may be coded in a complicated manner, and produces a perturbation on *any* system according to that rule which is built in. Now I bring the machine up to any system, and let it operate. I claim that we will not be able to describe in advance the output of this machine. I assert that all systems which are running in the normal anisotropic way will maintain a one-way flow of their coarse-grained properties, which will not change appreciably under this perturbation. Complicated systems of the other kind—for example the things that we build to make the film— will fall apart as soon as this machine touches them. The stability of this inverse is the thing I am denying.

As an example, consider the familiar case of gas in a box. Normally the experiment involves releasing the membrane permitting the gas to stream out so that the box comes to uniform pressure. If we now bring in the π machine, the gas still comes to uniform pressure. The gas is perhaps a little different, a little warmer, but that effect can be as

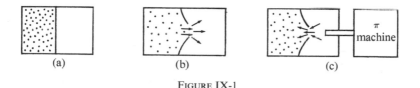

FIGURE IX-1

small as you like. But on the other hand, if we have a box like (c), one which we have artfully contrived so that all the gas is supposed to end up on one side as in case (a), then the output of the machine will make a major perturbation in the end result. The observer's problem is to contrive the final state in the presence of this π machine. It will make a greater or smaller perturbation on the outcome depending on how far off equilibrium the final contrived state is supposed to be. Of course, I cannot prove this, but I think that there is a strong case for this statement.

SCHIFF

But the final state can be contrived if we know what bit of the expansion of π the machine has picked. Then we do know what the machine is going to do next.

MORRISON

Your problem is to find out exactly where you are, in, say, 10^{50} digits of the π expansion. Only then will you know what comes next.

BONDI

It seems to me that this point is very much like the question of the difference in boundary conditions of elliptic and hyperbolic differential equations. If we try to solve the Laplace equation, given the function and its derivative on one surface, then analytically speaking we can get a solution, but it would be highly unstable, dependent on the conditions. Are you now saying that getting the stuff back into the box is a process that depends so unstably on the conditions that the process is not admissible in fact, just as solving Laplace's equation by giving the function and the normal derivative on one surface, although in principle possible, is not permissible because of extreme instability?

MORRISON

Yes. I try to demonstrate that instability by producing a model with a well-defined logical chain in the numbers in the expansion of π.

X

Are we assuming an irreversibility in time already?

MORRISON

No.

X

There is, say, a box of gas in which the atoms are all going to be on one side in the future. I have put the π machine in earlier. In this case the machine does not stop the atoms from going to one side of the box. In your case, the machine was introduced under different circumstances, still further in the past. The initial conditions are different. The machine can act in such a way that it helps to set up the contrived state. This depends on the rules of the game. But we are not allowed to do this in the real world because we are allowed to adjust only the present conditions. We have to leave to the free will of the machine what comes later. Is this a possible way of formulating the problem?

MORRISON

If you say that, then you must be able to determine what will always result from every chain of causes that can possibly exist. I agree that such a theory is conceivable, but such a theory must also include all the digits in π and all the details of the machine.

X

No. I do not include the digits of π. I specify only the future conditions without the present conditions.

MORRISON

Then your treatment will not satisfy the differential equations. This is also a possible position to take.

X

The same differential equations are satisfied if we specify the present conditions but do not specify the future conditions.

MORRISON

No, because the differential equations do not contain the Hamiltonian of the machine.

X

Neither do they in the other case where you put the box and machine together, in which case you calculate starting with initial conditions and end with different final conditions. The machine has an uncertainty of sorts in it, so the final conditions correspond to initial conditions that are uncertain, in a way of speaking. But is it not also possible to solve a problem in which the final conditions are the ones specified, and in which the different initial conditions of the machine are uncertain? Is this not a question of the rules of the game as opposed to a question of what conditions we have? I am trying to understand what you mean by "possible position." Do you mean that our issue is about practice or about analysis?

MORRISON

This is an example to illustrate a logical scheme which does not place the internal workings of the machine into the description.

BERGMANN

Do you remember the 1952 paper by Peierls in which he introduces a Lagrangian for two half-moons? For a perturbation to have a defined form, we must either fix the conditions at time minus infinity or at time plus infinity. An impressed perturbation would obviously derail the analysis at the other end. Now, in that π scheme, we have two possibilities. Either we fix conditions at minus infinity or at plus infinity. If we assume that when the machine is connected to the gas, the initial conditions are fixed in the past, then obviously the future events are affected. If conditions are fixed in the future, then the past events are affected.

GOLD

We beg the question to some extent in using the words "initial" and "final," because if we have not fixed what the sense of time is, then we ought to discuss initial and final things on the same level.

MORRISON

I am discussing them on the same level.

GOLD

You might as well have specified as the final condition that the gas is on one side of the box. Specify this condition correctly, and the gas will go there.

ROBINSON

But surely this is irrelevant to the argument. Let us be perverse and specify the initial conditions instead of the final conditions. Then if there is some disturbance which we cannot assess in advance, this will distinguish between normally running systems and those running backwards.

GOLD

There is a distinction in principle being made between initial and final conditions, the two ends of the experiment, a distinction which already contains in it something of the anisotropy of time.

ROSENFELD

I don't know whether I have understood Morrison's intention. But is it any different from the usual division of the extension in phase into regions corresponding to various configurations of the system? Then those regions will be intertwined in a very complicated way topologically in this many-dimensional extension. There will be one region corresponding to the equilibrium configuration which will fill most of the extension in phase, but it is intertwined with other regions corresponding to other configurations. Now a trajectory representing the life of the system will cross in succession all possible regions corresponding to the fluctuations around the equilibrium configuration of the system. But if we want by artificial initial conditions to remain in a region of the extension in phase corresponding to a rare configuration, then we have to fix those initial conditions very precisely, and the perturbations which we introduce will deviate the trajectory and inevitably bring it into the normal behavior.

MORRISON

That is the basis of what I say. What I argue is that the perturbation must be used in treatments which do not specify everything all the time.

BONDI

One might say instead that there are ways of starting from a particular place in phase space such that the different trajectories from it diverge wildly and those coming to it converge. This is similar to what happens in a simple dynamical system. Take the simple case of a rigid rotating body with three unequal axes of inertia. Everybody knows it does not spin stably about the intermediate axis, but of course we can say absolutely correctly that there is an infinite number of paths converging onto the unstable state. What we mean by "unstable" is that there are many paths going out of it. Since the motion is completely reversible, there must also be many paths going into the state. Nevertheless, this convergence is something that we do not in fact see, because as we follow a path coming in, the slightest disturbance will set the system on a path going out. Although we get a perfectly well-defined state from an initial perfectly well-defined state, this is not a sufficiently critical way of looking at the matter. Just as in the contrasting cases of elliptic and hyperbolic equations, we must consider whether from initial conditions confined to a small neighborhood we necessarily get a final solution confined to another small neighborhood.

GOLD

That argument is no more than the well-known consideration about behavior of a statistical system once it is understood that time goes. But you have already included that understanding, because otherwise you have not the slightest reason for singling out initial conditions from final conditions.

BONDI

No.

MORRISON

It is a different consideration because there is a perturbation in the system.

BONDI

That wouldn't be my answer. I would say that certain conditions could be used to start with. I do not care about the sense of time; it can go either way. There are conditions such that if the system is started in their neighborhood, the processes stay together either way they go, and there are other starting conditions under which the system is un- stable either way. I merely distinguish between stable and unstable initial conditions, and I look only at the point where information is put in. The sense of time is irrelevant.

HOYLE

For every perturbation is there not a convergent orbit to be made out of a divergent one?

BONDI

That is all right. There are zones where there are a lot of orbits crossing and going far away. There are zones where they all stay to- gether. This is surely the distinction. Either they stay together, or they diverge, or they converge. But it does not matter which way around we go. It can be that a slight derailment will always produce convergence.

ROSENFELD

An important point of thermodynamics should be considered in any discussion about the logical question of the sense of time. Thermo- dynamical states are timeless according to definition. They are, how- ever, not timeless in their effects on the actual world. When we speak of irreversibility in the statistical description, therefore, we have to consider the whole trajectory, from minus infinity to plus infinity. Of course, for every real situation, we start from initial conditions at a finite time. But for the consideration of the tendency for the coarse- grained density to become uniform we need to consider a limit over infinite time.

MORRISON

I would not like to put this statement in such an extreme form. What I wish to treat is the stability of the direction of statistical processes. The argument hangs on whether we are willing to include this perturbing system as another feature of the mechanical description. If we are willing to do this, then we have to include every perturbing system in the description. Insofar as this is concerned, I agree. But if we do not include every perturbing system, then only the stable directions will persist.

Suppose we put many systems in the box, and ask which way they evolve. We consider any one of them, measure its entropy, and then claim that it would be the same for all the others when the π machine has hit them all. Therefore we have established the sense of time. We call this the "arrowhead of time." This describes the evolution of a system in a stable sense. I do not use time.

BERGMANN

Yes, you do. In Figure IX-2(a) the system has been set up to go from

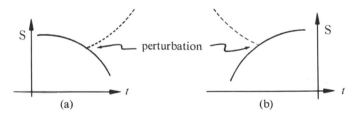

FIGURE IX-2

a more stable to a less stable state. There is a perturbation. The event of perturbation, even though the perturbation is small, will derail the system and make it go back to the more stable state. It will keep the molecules from congregating at one end of the box. Figure IX-2(b) is the mirror image of Figure IX-2(a), but with the positive time sense still in the same direction. We now have a system that "goes," in the ordinary sense of the word, to a more stable state. The whole past of this thing is derailed, and instead of coming from low entropy it is coming from high entropy.

MORRISON

But because this perturbation can be arbitrarily small, the whole system has infinitely many possible pasts.

BERGMANN

If you put in a perturbation, either the path in (a) gets changed *or* the path in (b) gets changed. If you decide not to touch the past, then the perturbation affects only the future. The other diagram represents the opposite decision; instead of derailing the future, you derail the past.

MORRISON

The number of times that the machine works in order to accomplish that is very small.

X

It depends on the rules of the game. You even mentioned the possibility of using several different π machines. Here is the real question on which everything turns: What is now kept the same in comparing all these π machines? Is it the initial conditions? Is it the final conditions? Is it the position of the seventy-fourth molecule at a particular time?

MORRISON

The micro-description is kept the same.

X

But that cannot be so, because for different disturbances the micro-descriptions are going to be different. They all satisfy different equations, since the states of the π machines are different. We cannot specify the microstate at all times.

MORRISON

Yes, we can. We can specify it at the time of the interactions.

X

Well, the interactions last for a certain period of time, so let's not try to sneak around. You are imagining that there is a certain moment at which you can make all the machines more or less the same. Then you say that at another moment they are either very different or statistically more or less the same. This is the stability question. I am trying to understand the rules of the game which do not permit me, for example, to specify something else the same in all these machines, such as the final conditions. This is an open question.

ROBINSON

I have just gone through a fit of profound introspection, and it seems to me that in order to set up initial conditions, we watch the system evolving. We are then puzzled as to whether the system is evolving into the future or into the past, having become a little disoriented in the course of listening to a lecture.

BERGMANN

I think that there is a real case in which this happens. This is in the world which the gypsy reads out of the tea leaves. If the customer happens to be female, then there is a tall, dark, handsome man in her future; all disturbances such as black cats have to be rearranged so as to bring about this future state of affairs.

BONDI

Let us consider the example of the box of gas. In this case, we can consider an instant when conditions are given. It has been very clearly shown that there are certain conditions which we are allowed to give and others which we are not allowed to give, because of instability. We may give conditions in which all the gas is on one side; we may not give the other kind of conditions. Dynamically speaking, when we have such given conditions we can calculate one way in time and the other way in time equally well. The evolution is completely symmetrical. A sense of time has been introduced only in our technical ability to set up the system in the past for future development, and not the system in the future for past development.

MORRISON

I claim that whichever way we calculate, we must either introduce time by making this choice, or else we must work out every chain of causes.

GOLD

We can do that only if we are able to look at the system at the present and in the future. We are unable to do this in reverse because we are apparently "ticking" along a time axis which is already a defined thing for our own evolution. If we were God, we could dash down at any time in the past or future arbitrarily, and we could say, "We will fix the conditions now and we will look at the system then." The "now" and the "then" are in relation to our natural "ticking" along the time axis. One way is the "past"; the other way is the "future." They are all the same.

MORRISON

The π machine runs just as well backwards as it runs forwards.

GOLD

But the godlike view covers the whole description including the tape machine. It then gives the results of Bergmann's diagram.

MORRISON

On the other hand, such a view must cover every class of perturbations, even those not specified.

SALPETER

I have a question which is not so much about past and future, but is really the mathematical question, "Can we do it?" This concerns boundary conditions. Suppose there are argon molecules and oxygen molecules in the box. Can we state for one end of time that all of the argon molecules are to be on one side of the box, and state for the other end of time that the oxygen molecules are all on one side? This is a kind of circumstance we do not often meet, regardless of which is "before" and which is "after." Are we unable to do this, from the mathematical point of view? At first sight we might think that we would specify the same number of conditions in this case as we usually do, but is there something inconsistent in this?

MORRISON

I think this circumstance is consistent, but it is terribly unstable. The slightest error in the specification of any one of the coordinates either way will mess the thing up in both ways.

GOLD

In previous cases we were allowed just one boundary specification free from instability. In Salpeter's case, we do not have even one.

ROSENFELD

The whole problem of statistical mechanics can be formulated without reference to a sense of time. All we are concerned about is defining, or giving a rule for, the time average of a given quantity which is a function of the phase space coordinates. In general, all we can say about such a time average is its limit for infinite time, the time average taken from minus infinity to plus infinity. This we can prove under suitable conditions to be represented by a phase average corresponding to the uniformity of the distribution of the coarse-grained density over the energy shell. This establishes the correspondence between the mechanical quantities and the macroscopic thermodynamic quantities. From this we can define the laws of thermodynamics. Now, irreversibility is introduced there, exactly as Bondi said, because when we consider transitions between different microscopically defined states, the trajectories going through rare configurations are unstable. Those trajectories exist, but in technical language they have measure zero in the extension in phase, and therefore they do not really contribute in the averaging.

MORRISON

The only place in this summary where I would demur is in the integration over an infinite range, which I think implies an assumption that I try to avoid. If we make this assumption, then clearly we have to involve ourselves deeply with the whole cosmological question. Of course, I deny the existence of a decoupled system of infinite duration, with the exception, of the universe itself. However, any subsystem will demonstate these results to some degree, provided that the system has a sufficiently complicated structure. The orbital motion of the earth, for example, is perfectly stable to small perturbations and therefore provides no distinction in time direction.

HOYLE

Have you not chosen one class of perturbation and omitted the other classes?

MORRISON

Yes. I say only that if the presence of these correlations is admitted, then we cannot stop short of correlating the whole bloody mess from start to finish. As far as I can see, the existence of this independent chain of causes is a sufficient condition for doing this job, and its absence is at least implied by the description which we consider to be complete.

BONDI

The π machine serves only to impress the importance of stability considerations on those who might not otherwise agree.

GOLD

We cannot ignore the fact that entropy increases. The sense of entropy increase is given by a loss of information from the systems. "Loss of information" implies that the system is on an unstable path, so that we would have to know things very precisely in order to be able to make predictions. This whole thing is only a discussion of the fact that entropy increases. That seems to me still the basic problem we are trying to understand. Why is it that we have the asymmetry given to us? We can recognize it everywhere.

ROSENFELD

I think that the answer to that is implied in the conditions of observation. It is because we pose the problem in a particular way.

GOLD

It is because we pose the problem with a distinction between an "initial" and a "final" condition. Once the pattern on the wall is given, the question why we think that we follow it by tracing out a world line is quite separate. That would fix what we call an "initial condition" and what we call a "final condition."

MORRISON

I quite disagree. If that pattern is in the least degree incomplete, then we are forced into the position I have outlined.

X

Incorrect. Following Salpeter's suggestion, suppose that we have oxygen and argon molecules in the box, and suppose that it is possible to specify the following: that the oxygen molecules are all in the left side of the box at $t = -1$ hour, and that the argon molecules are all on the left side of the box at a time $t = +1$ hour. If this can be done, then the output of the machine is irrelevant. Consider a whole sequence of states, each with a definite π machine. We have a corresponding sequence of solutions. It is true that the positions of the oxygen molecules in the future are very sensitive to the output of the machines, but the positions of the argon molecules in the future are not, because these are specified. If we now consider the sequence of states, have we got stability or instability? The sequence is stable for one kind of molecule and unstable for the other; one species of the gas has entropy going one way, and in the other it goes the other way. This seems to be a logical possibility unless we know more about the dynamics.

MORRISON

One half of the molecules is going to do something odd. One half of them is going to go the wrong way from the point of view of the π machines that have their curious conditions.

GOLD

You seem to imply by the word "unstable" that the system will be arranging itself in a more random fashion in what you choose to think of as the "future."

MORRISON

No. I do not care what happens to the system as long as the many π machines do not agree. There will be all kinds of different concentrations of the mixture as it evolves. That would not be the case with other specifications, for example where the oxygen and argon are both specified at a given time.

X

I do not see why you say that. Why should there be any less tendency in the one case than in the other?

BONDI

Consider a tube in phase space which bulges toward one end or the other. Now the tube in X's example represents a phase space divided in two by a plane, argon on one side, and oxygen on the other. One half of the tube expands in one direction; the other half expands in the other direction. This is no more symmetrical than giving a phase space tube which is narrow and expands towards both ends.

MORRISON

I thought the rules were to be specified ahead of time.

BERGMANN

But "ahead of time" means "at any time prior to perturbation."

X

It strikes me as interesting that partial initial and partial final conditions might have been the condition of the universe. It is interesting to ask what kind of feelings we would have under other circumstances about the future and the past.

BERGMANN

This arrangement would satisfy both the teleologists and the causalists. In this case, the universe is arranged causally as far as gross physical effects such as increase of entropy are concerned, but with a definite fixed "moral" purpose in the future! That makes everybody happy!

MORRISON

The only question is whether that is true!

BERGMANN

I don't think it is, but that is only because I am intolerant!

X

The universe we live in is so all-pervading, and our experience is so closely connected to it, that a considerable exercise of imagination is required to ask any of these questions. If we discuss these questions, we must exert great imagination to conceive of worlds that do not exist. One of these imaginary situations that has always bothered me is the kind of world in which the future is partially specified and the past is in the intermediate region. How would it look if we were all directed towards some ultimate goal?

ROSENFELD

This may be a dangerous extrapolation, because when we speak of initial conditions and final conditions we are thinking of usual situations in which we are dealing with small systems. In this case we are in a position to substantiate the extrapolation, but extrapolating the whole universe from what we can know is risky.

GOLD

I had hoped that Morrison would say something about the relation between the flow of information and the flow of matter. Information content is clearly related to the actual positions and momenta of the particles in question. Predicting or retrodicting the motion of matter is clearly dependent upon this relation. I feel that my idea of an arrow of time arises and appears to be so definite because of this relation. Part of the pattern of the world lines could be an information-flow diagram which is closely related to the rest of the pattern. We would expect to find that the anisotropy of the main pattern was in fact responsible for making a general displacement of the information-flow diagram, so as to imply a lag in the sense in which time is customarily said to progress.

The anisotropy in the main pattern may be due originally to different boundary conditions at the two ends of time. It is this anisotropy which is closely related to what we term the "expansion" of the universe. We can consider this anisotropy to be responsible for the unsymmetrical relation between the pattern of world lines and the information-flow diagram which might be drawn for a particular human mind or a particular computing machine. This asymmetry then gives to us or to computing machines the notion of progressing time. This would not be so if the patterns of world lines were isotropic. The information-flow diagrams could thus not possess an anisotropy which is opposite to the anisotropy of the flow of matter.

MORRISON

But we must acquire information by the expenditure of free energy. This implies an irreversible entropic process from the start. Anyhow, if the universe were shown to be symmetrical on the large scale, we would still have to give time directions to local physical processes, because it is the bits of the pattern which force us to the directionality.

GOLD

That I do not believe. If that pattern is symmetrical, then we have no way in which to give an orientation of the whole diagram.

GRÜNBAUM

If there were as much bona fide precognitive knowledge as memory knowledge, then the asymmetry would disappear.

GOLD

Yes. If the pattern of flow of matter has no anisotropy in it to begin with, then the pattern of the flow of information would certainly not have asymmetry in it. It is not even very clear whether it would mean anything. There is no derived quantity which we can make out of that pattern that possesses the anisotropy which the pattern itself did not possess. The information is a quantity derived out of the pattern on the wall, and if the pattern on the wall had an asymmetry in it, then the derived quantity, namely what we call information, will have some property that can fix an arrow which we use subjectively. I think this is the basis of the subjective arrow.

MORRISON

You are saying that noise introduces information as often as it disturbs it in a symmetrical world. I just do not believe that.

GOLD

I am not even sure what information would mean in a symmetrical world, but I cannot make an anisotropic flow of information, if that means anything, in a pattern which is isotropic.

LAYZER

In all these discussions we tend to talk about temporarily isolated branch systems because we know the physics. In point of fact, we could have concentrated on quite different systems, open systems like people or trees or crystals, in which the arrow of time is quite as marked, but is actually going just the other way. I think this is a basic part of the problem. It is necessary to look at both aspects—the increasing entropy in branch systems and the decreasing entropy of open systems—within a single framework that can give both aspects.

WHEELER

Can we talk in a consistent way about a universe in different parts of which the direction of information flow is different? N. Wiener discussed the situation of beings whose time senses run oppositely. According to him all communication between such beings is out of the question. A being whose time sense were directed oppositely to ours could not be observed by us. Any signal that he might send us would reach us with a logical stream of consequence from his point of view, antecedence from our point of view. These antecedents, said Wiener, would already be in our experience. We would therefore try to make a natural explanation of the content of his signal without presupposing an intelligent being. Its meaning would seem to be as fortuitous as the faces we read into mountains and cliffs.

SCHIFF

This requires that the being with opposite time sense lives in a different world. He cannot live in our world, where chemical reactions go with increasing entropy.

X

Let me try to make an example of such a situation. Consider two boxes that are separated from one another. We study all the dynamical circumstances in which the positions of the molecules in one box are specified at the origin at a past time and the positions of the molecules in the other box are specified at a future time. Then we may average over little disturbances if we want to, but in studying the ensemble of these systems we make sure that the initial conditions in one box are specified and the final conditions in the other box are specified, and that the boxes have relatively weak interactions with each other. They can interact with each other by signaling back and forth. Now if there is no interaction between the boxes, or if, so to speak, we do not consider both boxes at once, we would, because of the laws of dynamics, allow the situation in which the conditions are specified in the future to duplicate a reverse motion relative to the axis of time in the other box, where things go to order from disorder. I think that Wiener is trying to discuss that situation, or one analogous to it, and I do not think that this situation is self-evidently impossible.

SCHIFF

I object primarily to Morrison's view that the two boxes must function in the same external world with strong coupling. This is impossible. We must have two almost isolated boxes with just enough weak coupling so that they can interchange signals.

MORRISON

If the boxes are sufficiently large, then they will affect each other in a serious way no matter how weak the coupling is.

BONDI

The problem is not that they interact directly, but that the interaction is so pervasive that there is no local reversal. This is the question that Wiener really raises.

WHEELER

The coupling by radiation between these time-opposed systems presents very difficult problems because the direction of radiation flow is ambiguous. As Wiener says, "Thus the part of the universe which we see must have its past-future relations, as far as emission of radiation is concerned, concordant with our own. The very fact that we see a star means that its thermodynamics is like our own" [*Cybernetics* (New York: Wiley & Sons, 1948)]. To me it is not at all obvious that this is the case, because a star that is operating the other way must be sucking up energy, so it would clear up those black spots on the film and restore it to pristine emulsion.

X

No. The film is in a standard condition. When we expose a film very carefully, then look at it, there are some spots on it due to the heat from the background radiation, even if there is no image. But this star is sucking energy away from the plate. It takes energy into the future. The energy is going from the plate in a focus to the star, so it would make the background radiation less on the plate.

BERGMANN

Yes. This is a device for defogging plates!

BONDI

Perhaps we have to distinguish here between two kinds of photons, those from the ordinary world and those being sucked up by the "plate-defogging" star.

X

Of course, the entire world is "ordinary" in the physical sense. It is the boundary conditions, the initial and final conditions, which matter.

We are supposing these to be possible. We still have not found the answer to Salpeter's question about whether mixed conditions are dynamically allowable. If we imagine a whole ensemble of universes in which the past conditions are specified in one locale and the future conditions are specified in another locale, as the light and all the other things are definite mechanical things, then we can have definite answers to all these questions.

GOLD

I think that the specification problem for mixed conditions implies having a complete calculation of the system. Otherwise we cannot know what interrelation we must have between the two sets of conditions in order to make the conditions complete. The question of whether or not we can have mixed conditions is related only to the difficulty of calculation. There might be some mathematical impossibility.

X

The laws of dynamics and the initial conditions limit the possible worlds. In other words, the set of worlds we should consider form an ensemble which fits the laws of mechanics plus the initial and final conditions. I am not going to worry about the problem of how hard it would be to calculate such a thing.

BERGMANN

The universe is just an analogue computer which tries to figure out what a sophisticated digital computer would do!

MORRISON

Can cosmology give the time direction? I do not see how it can unless it can be proved impossible to build a box which is decoupled thermodynamically from the rest of the universe. I could spend my life in an air-raid shelter, for instance. I have no wish personally to get into thermal equilibrium; I only wish to have a shelter big enough so that within it I can make a small subsystem that is close to thermal equilibrium. I can guarantee to do this, provided I have an energy source. I can scramble any subsystem out of equilibrium with this free energy. The shelter still has a thermodynamic sense of time.

X

The whole conception of energy source is the key to cosmology. We all agree that everywhere in the real world time goes the same way. You cannot deny that you must build your air-raid shelter out of stuff which is originally interacting with the whole universe, and which has the "sign" of its time determined.

MORRISON

Surely you seem to be going back on your remarks with regard to light signals, then. Light signals are not important any more as far as I am concerned. All I need is a source of energy. I need no information except what is in the energy.

BONDI

But you cannot create disequilibrium of the matter in your air-raid shelter once the shelter is in equilibrium. We agree on that, so you must introduce the disequilibrium at some stage from the outside before you shut the door. What we claim is that the matter of disequilibrium which you bring in is the "memory" of the universe, so to speak.

MORRISON

You say that this disequilibrium is a sort of "imprint" of the rest of the universe, but nowhere do I see any signaling between the shelter and the universe. I do not need the arrow of time forever, but only for a finite time. I am prepared for its eventual disappearance. To impair my case you would have to show that a contracting universe contains no pools of energy, or that a static universe contains none.

GOLD

Allow me to quote from my paper [*Am. J. Phys.*, **30** (1962), 403] one brief paragraph which I think bears strongly upon our present discussion. "The same rule applies to all systems; interference from without enables them to show time's arrow, and this may persist for some time after the interference has ceased. All completely internal effects may reflect the physical laws that apply and all these are then strictly time symmetrical. On whatever scale we choose our system, we have to go to a larger scale to understand how it is contrived to show the arrow of time."

MORRISON

Then you certainly agree that I can, with free energy, construct a system which is out of disequilibrium and watch its time arrow vanish.

LAYZER

It seems there are two questions relevant to this general discussion. First, is the universe relevant at all? Second, is it relevant in a way that Gold and Bondi and the others would like it to be, in a sort of continuous, global interaction? I find this hard to believe.

X

The question we have before us is only whether it is possible to have a contracting universe in which light is emitted by the stars, and in which the thermodynamics goes forward in time. The problem for these gentlemen is to prove that such a thing is impossible.

BONDI

The difficulty of deciding the issue which Morrison has raised is that there is a customs officer at the entrance to his air-raid shelter, and they have a disagreement about which articles have to be declared as containing information about the universe. Surely the answer to his question whether there can be a contracting universe in which radiation emerges from the stars is given by Olbers' paradox.

MORRISON

We have other possibilities for avoiding the paradox. The universe could be finite, for example. In this sense, we are faced only with the question whether we can understand the various cosmologies. What you are striving to show is that there exists a unique set of assumptions for the distant future from which every bit of physics which we know will follow.

GOLD

It could be that we can trace in detail the thermodynamic evolution relative to the direction of the cosmological expansion. We may find that for all cases of expansion the time arrow goes the same way. We can describe such a universe satisfactorily with time-symmetrical electrodynamics. Then it would make just as much sense to say that this is a contracting universe in which radiation comes from the diffused matter and focuses down on the stars, and in which the thermodynamics is all backwards.

MORRISON

Then I can build an air-raid shelter under the specifications which I stated, such that the thermodynamics in one of its subsystems will go forwards.

BONDI

It seems to me that we can divide the information about the universe into two parts: its state when the stars began to shine and its subsequent motion. It is immediately obvious that the subsequent motion will be important only after a sufficiently long time. So any condition at a later time depends on the initial conditions and on the subsequent motion. The relative importance of these two kinds of information changes with the elapsed time. We can then surely show that after a sufficiently long time it is the motion of the universe rather than the initial state that makes any difference insofar as the arrow of time is determined by the universe. We therefore naturally wonder whether we can account for the arrow of time without referring back to the initial conditions, and that seems to me to be the problem. We can have a consistent model with a contraction if we start the contraction just after the stars begin to shine. This system is quite consistent, but the question is how long it can stay in this condition.

X

We make the assumption that time has an infinity in one direction. It might be impossible to get a thermodynamically consistent theory without taking that direction to be the future. I do not know. But I am not going to get into a debate in which I am required to keep the process going forever either way, because that already begs part of the question. If the universe is finite on either end of the time axis, then it can either contract or expand, or stand still, or even start in one spot and end up somewhere else.

BERGMANN

In the question of the decoupled subsystem we may be mixing up a number of different time scales. Assuming simply the laws of classical mechanics, what is the time period necessary for an isolated system on the order of moles, or what we would call a laboratory system, to go through a Poincaré cycle? Is not the scale longer than, say, 10^{80} years?

At any rate, it is long compared to the inverse Hubble constant. If the system runs through only a small fraction of a Poincaré cycle, a general theorem can be applied to it. The theorem states that if the system starts in a state of disequilibrium, it undergoes essentially a monotonic relaxation for a very long period of time. Now, "very long" might mean "long compared to the age of the universe." If we bury somebody in an air-raid shelter while in a state of disequilibrium, and if our universe should be an oscillatory universe which reverses itself every 10^{10} to 10^{11} years, the victim will still be approaching equilibrium even after several "cycles."

X

I wonder if we could allow for a special property of oscillating universes. Suppose that when such a universe attains its maximum size, all velocities become zero and thence reverse, so that all the motions reverse; thus the universe as a whole is reversible. This property could be formulated as a special law in the form of a boundary condition. Of course, it would have to be formulated statistically, but that can be done in principle. This property does not allow complete freedom of will. We cannot put the person in the air-raid shelter with just any initial condition. Hidden in the initial conditions of the air-raid shelter there are bits of information at the microscopic level which impose the boundary conditions. According to this, just at the moment in which the universe attains its maximum size, the matter in the shelter must reverse its motion.

MORRISON

But this means that the universe must be described in advance with transcendental information, if the shelter is completely isolated.

BERGMANN

In this case we have no freedom of choice as to when the shelter may be reopened. It must be reopened at an instant which is exactly symmetric in time from the instant of its closing.

LAYZER

Should this condition be like a conservation law hidden among the other physical laws, or does it suffice to say that this new boundary condition is a deep law of physics which is consistent with, but independent of, all the other laws?

X

This condition is something like the idea that we now use to understand the one-sidedness of the world. It is the requirement of past conditions in a certain form. We can reverse the velocities of particles in a system to get back to a low-entropy state from a high-entropy state only if we have the information suitable for the job. This special condition is not given at the moment of creation, but at the state of maximum expansion where everything reverses.

X. The Anisotropy of Time[1]

A. GRÜNBAUM

Summary

In §1, the bona fide anisotropy of physical time is sharply distinguished from the so-called one-way *forward* flow of time, constituted by the *coming into being* of future events.

The importance of making this distinction is then demonstrated in §2 by showing that in contrast to the anisotropy of time, the presumed phenomenon of one-way forward flow of time has no status whatever in physics. Instead, the forward flow of time—in so far as it exists at all—depends essentially on the existence of organisms which *conceptually register* (ideationally represent) physical events by becoming *aware* of them through the effects produced by them in consciousness. Next, reasons are given for denying the contention of numerous past and present writers that, in an *indeterministic* world such as that of quantum mechanics, as opposed to a *deterministic* world like that of classical physics, there is a "coming into being" of events along one of two distinguished senses of time. For it is argued that the purported phenomenon of events coming into being cannot depend on the indeterministic character of the laws linking physical events in space and time; instead, the coming *into* existence of a physical event is constituted by the *entry* of some of its *effects* into the "now" of the conceptualizing awareness possessed by humans and possibly other entities. Since coming into being thus depends on a *causal* process, it requires a degree of macrodeterminism sufficient to assure a high correlation between the occurrence of a physical event and our being made aware of it.

The logical havoc produced for physics by the pseudoconception of a "forward flow" of physical time is then illustrated as follows: it is argued that this pseudoconception vitiates P. W. Bridgman's objections to Eddington's thermodynamic account of the anisotropy of time, although it is recognized that Eddington's account is unsatisfactory for *other* reasons.

In §3, it is maintained that within the framework of a certain set of physical theories, which permit a sharp distinction between boundary conditions and laws, the existence of *irreversible* physical processes can be asserted on the basis of obtaining *boundary conditions*, but *not* on the basis of the laws. And it is further maintained that the irreversibility claimed by this set of theories does *not* char-

149

acterize the long-term behavior of systems which are both spatially finite *and* permanently closed but rather other types of systems.

The generation of irreversibility by boundary conditions is discussed first in the thermodynamic context of the (coarse-grained) classical entropy behavior of so-called "branch-systems," important divergences from H. Reichenbach's treatment of these ubiquitous systems being pointed out. As a corollary of the anisotropy of time existing in that type of thermodynamic context, attention is called to the following: (a) why under some specified conditions, we can have records of a certain kind of past event but not of that same kind of future event, and (b) why under different specified conditions, information concerning a physical state s_1 permits the prediction of a specific later state s_2, while information regarding that state s_2 does *not* allow the *retrodiction* of the specific earlier state s_1.

In §4, it is emphasized that irreversibility due to boundary conditions also characterizes physical processes which are *non*thermodynamic in the sense of extending into an infinite space, so that no Boltzmannian entropy is defined for them.

In conclusion, it is recognized that the scope of the preceding discussion ought to be enlarged to include further physical theories such as the steady-state cosmology. And it is noted that with respect to that wider class of physical theories, the connection between the thermodynamic and nonthermodynamic kinds of irreversibility (i.e., unreversedness!) may well turn out to be a good deal deeper than this paper has claimed. Specifically, the connection may go beyond the fact that both kinds of irreversibility are due to boundary conditions rather than to laws and fail to obtain in the case of systems which are both spatially finite and permanently closed.

§1. *The Distinction between the Anisotropy of Time and the Alleged "One-Way Forward Flow" of Time*

Just as we can coordinatize one of the dimensions of space by means of real numbers *without* being committed to the anisotropy of that spatial dimension, so also we can coordinatize a topologically open time continuum without being committed to the existence of irreversible kinds of processes which would render that continuum anisotropic. For so long as the states of the world (as defined by some one simultaneity criterion) are ordered by a relation of temporal *betweenness* having the same formal properties as the spatial betweenness on a Euclidean straight line, there will be two time senses which are opposite to each other. And we can then assign increasing real-number coordinates in one of these senses and decreasing ones in the other by convention *without* assuming that these two senses are *further distinguished* by the structural property that some kinds of sequences of states encountered along one of them are never (or hardly ever) encountered along the other. Thus, we can use the locutions "initial state," "final state," "before," and "after" on the basis of such a time-coordinatization, entirely without prejudice to whether the two ordinally opposite time senses turn out to be further distinguished structurally.

If the latter situation does indeed obtain because of the existence of *irreversible* kinds of processes, then the time continuum is anisotropic. By the same token, if the temporal inverses of all kinds of processes belonging to a certain very wide class actually materialized, then time would be isotropic with respect to that important class of process-types.

It is clear that the anisotropy of time resulting from the existence of irreversible processes consists in the mere structural differences between the two opposite senses of time but provides no basis at all for singling out *one* of the two opposite senses as "*the* direction" of time. Hence the assertion that irreversible processes render time anisotropic is *not at all* equivalent to such statements as "time flows one way." And the metaphor of time's "arrow," which Eddington intended to refer to the anisotropy of time, can be misleading: attention to the head of the arrow to the exclusion of the tail may suggest that there is a "flow" in *one* of the two anisotropically related senses. Indeed, as we shall see later on, P. W. Bridgman and others were misled into supposing that Eddington was claiming that time progresses or goes in one of two opposite directions, namely "forward."

Since the instants of anisotropic time are ordered by the relation "earlier than" no less than by the converse relation "later than," the anisotropy of time provides no warrant at all for singling out the "later than" sense as "the" direction of time. Instead, the inspiration for speaking about "the" direction of time derives from the supposition that there is a transient "now" or "present" which can be claimed to shift so as to single out the future direction of time as the sense of its "advance."

But this supposition is vitiated by a logical blunder. For the term "shift" is used in its literal kinematic sense in such a way that the spatial direction of a shift is determined by noting where the shifting object is at *later* times. Hence when we speak of the "now" as "shifting" in time or along the time axis, we use this term in such a way that it is simply a matter of *definition* that the "now" shifts or advances in the future direction. This declaration is a pure tautology, since it says that later nows are later than earlier ones, which is no more true than that earlier nows are earlier than later ones. By the same token, the words "flow" and "come into being" are used in such a way that assertions like "time flows unidirectionally from past to future" and "events come into being as we move into the future" are tautologies and thus cannot codify any factual property of time.

Apart from its minor usage to designate an arbitrarily chosen event of reference in the Minkowski diagram, the term "now" functions as an anthropocentric designation whose referent is mind-dependent; what is "now" about a physical event is that some of its immediate effects *are conceptualized as being presented* to the conscious *awareness* of one or more (human) perceivers. And if a (human or other conceptualizing) perceiver proceeds to express that awareness in a linguistic utterance, the quasi-simultaneity of the physical event with that utterance is an indicator of the nowness of the physical event in question. Thus, in the first instance, nowness is an attribute of experienced events which are being *consciously* registered and conceptualized as occurring, and the awareness of this now-content can coincide with an awareness of other events as remembered and of still others as envisioned. Psychological or common-sense time is constituted by the ordered *diversity* of the "now-contents" of conscious awareness, these now-contents being ordered with respect to the relations "earlier than" and "later than." Hence, the *diversity* of the now-contents allows us to regard as a fact the "transient" division of psychological time into past and future by the "now" of conceptualizing awareness. But if this factual statement is not to turn into a tautology, the transiency of the "now" must be understood as mere diversity, that is, as directionally neutral with respect to the past and the future.

§2. *The Dependence of "Coming into Being" on Conceptualizing Consciousness, and the Irrelevance of Indeterminism to "Coming into Being"*

I have maintained that the transient now with respect to which the distinction between the past and the future of common sense and psychological time acquires meaning has no relevance at all to the time of physical events. For the now ingredient in classifying events as past, present, or future has no significance at all apart from the egocentric perspectives of a *conscious*, conceptualizing organism and from the immediate experiences of that organism. If this contention is correct, it has an important consequence: Since an event comes into being by occurring *now, the coming into being or becoming of an event, as distinct from its mere tenseless occurrence at a certain time, is thus no more than the entry of some of its temporally proximate effects into the immediate awareness of a conceptualizing organism (man)*. Hermann Weyl has given a beautiful metaphorical statement of the dependence of coming *into* being on consciousness by writing: "The objective world simply *is*, it does not *happen*. Only to the gaze of my consciousness, crawling upward along the life [i.e., world-] line of my body, does a section of this world come to life as a fleeting image in space which continuously changes in time."[2] An event simply *"is"* by occurring tenselessly at a certain clock time t. If true, the tenseless assertion that an event E occurs at the time t_0 can truly be made at all times t other than t_0 no less than at the time t_0. But if at a given clock time t_0 it is true to say of a particular event E that it is *happening at present* or occurring *now*, then this claim could *not* also be truly made at all other times $t \neq t_0$. By the same token, the *tensed* assertion that an event E happens *at present* must not be identified with the tenseless assertion that the event E occurs or *"is present"* at time t_0. Weyl is here contrasting happening at present with tenseless occurrence at a certain clock time t_0.

The contention that coming *into* being (or "becoming") is *not* a property of *physical* events themselves but only of human or other conscious awareness of these events has been denied by a number of past and present authors. Thus, authors such as A. S. Eddington, H. Reichenbach, H. Bondi, and G. J. Whitrow have claimed that if physical events in space and time are linked by *indeterministic* laws, as in quantum physics, then there is a mind-independent basis for the "coming into being" of physical events along the future direction of time via the transiency of the "now." I now wish to explain by reference to the statements of Reichenbach and Bondi why I regard this claim to be incorrect.

Reichenbach contends that "when we speak about the progress of time [from earlier to later] . . . , we intend to make a synthetic [i.e., factual] assertion which refers both to an immediate experience and to physical reality."[3] And he thinks that this assertion about events coming *into* being can be justified in regard to physical reality on the basis of indeterministic quantum mechanics by the following argument:[4] In classical deterministic physics, both the past and the future were determined in relation to the present by one-to-one functions even though they differed in that there could be direct observational records of the past and only predictive inferences concerning the future. On the other hand, while the results of past measurements on a quantum-mechanical system are *determined* in relation to the present by the present *records* of these measurements, a present measurement of one of two conjugate quantities does *not* uniquely determine in any way the result of a *future* measurement of the other conjugate quantity. Hence, Reichenbach concludes that "the concept of 'becoming' acquires significance in physics: the present, which separates the future from the past, is the moment at which that which was undetermined becomes determined, and 'becoming' has the same meaning as 'becoming determined.' . . . It is with respect to 'now' that the past is determined and that the future is not."

My reasons for rejecting this argument are the following. In the indeterministic quantum world, the relations between the sets of measurable values of the state variables characterizing a physical system at different times are, in principle, *not* the one-to-one relations linking the states of classically behaving closed systems. But this holds *now* for a given state of a physical system and its absolute future quite independently of whether that state occurs at midnight on December 31, 1800, or at noon on March 1, 1984. Nay, if we consider *any one* of the temporally successive regions of space-time, we can veridically assert the following at *any* time: the events belonging to that particular region's absolute past could be (more or less) uniquely specified in records which are a part of that region, whereas its particular absolute future is thence quantum-mechanically unpredictable. Accordingly, *every* event, be it that of Plato's birth or that of a person to be born in the year 2000 A.D., *at all times* constitutes a divide in Reichenbach's sense between its own recordable past and its unpredictable future, thereby satisfying Reichenbach's definition of the "present" at any and all times! And if Reichenbach were to reply that the indeterminacies of the events of the year of Plato's birth have already been transformed into a determinacy, whereas those of 2000 A.D. have not, then the rejoinder would be: This tensed statement holds for *our* present conscious now in 1963, but not for the nows of those having experiences after 2000 A.D. Accordingly, contrary to Reichenbach, the now of conceptual awareness must be invoked tacitly at time *t*, if the instant *t* is to be nonarbitrarily and uniquely singled out at time *t* as being now.

If I did not misunderstand him, Bondi also claimed that in an indeterministic universe physical events distinctively come into being when he wrote: "In a theory with indeterminacy, . . . the passage of time transforms statistical expectation into real events."[5] If Bondi intended this statement to assert that the indeterminacy makes for our human inability to know in advance of their actual occurrence what particular kinds of events will in fact materialize, then, of course, there can be no objection. For in an indeterministic world, the attributes of specified kinds of events are indeed not uniquely fixed by the properties of earlier events and are therefore correspondingly unpredictable. But I take him to affirm beyond this the following traditional philosophical doctrine: The *existential* status of *future* events in an indeterministic world is that of coming *into* being with time, whereas in a deterministic world it is one of simply occurring. And my objection to this view is that in a (microphysically) indeterministic physical world, the coming into being of an event as distinct from its mere tenseless occurrence depends on somebody's becoming suitably *aware* of it, just as in a classically deterministic one. For what is the character and import of the difference between these two worlds in regard to the determinateness of future events? The difference concerns only the type of functional connection linking the attributes of future events to those of present or past events. Thus, *in relation to the states existing at other times*, an indeterministic universe allows alternatives as to the attributes of an event that occurs at some given time, whereas a deterministic universe provides no corresponding latitude. But this difference does *not* enable (microphysical) indeterminism to make for a precipitation of future events *into existence* in a way in which determinism does not. In either a deterministic or indeterministic universe, events can be held to *become* "actual" in the sense of becoming *present to our awareness;* but becoming actual in virtue of occurring *now* must *not* be confused with a spurious mind-independent coming into existence *per se*.

Nor does indeterminacy as contrasted with determinacy make for any difference whatever at any time in regard to the *attribute-specificity* of the future events themselves. For in either kind of universe, it is a fact of logic that what will be will be, no less than what is present or past is indeed present or past![6] The result of a future quantum-mechanical measurement may not be definite prior to its occurrence in relation to earlier states, and thus our prior knowledge of it correspondingly cannot be definite. But as an event, it is as fully attribute-definite and thus occurs no less than a measurement made in a deterministic world does.

Two quite different things seem to be confused when it is inferred that in an indeterministic world the future events distinctively come into being with the passage of time over and above merely becoming observed, whereas in a deterministic universe they do not: (1) the *epistemological* precipitation of the *de facto* event-properties of future events out of the wider matrix of the possible properties allowed by the quantum-mechanical probabilities, a precipitation which is constituted by our getting to know these *de facto* properties, and (2) an *existential* coming into being over and above merely becoming observed. The *epistemological* precipitation is indeed affected by the passage of time through the transformation of a merely statistical expectation into a definite piece of information. But this does *not* show that in an indeterministic world, there obtains any kind of *precipitation into existence or coming into being* with the passage of time that does not also obtain in a deterministic one. Nay, far from depending on the indeterministic character of the laws linking physical events, the coming into being of such events depends on the existence of a considerable degree of *macro*-determinism; since the coming into being of an event is constituted by the entry of some of its effects into the now of awareness, its coming into being depends on a causal process which must be sufficiently macrodeterministic to assure a high correlation between the occurrence of the event and our being made suitably aware of it.

We see then that the events of the indeterministic quantum world do not come into being any more than those of the classical deterministic world. And my earlier contention that the transient now is mind-dependent and irrelevant to physics therefore stands.

The failure to be cognizant of the physical irrelevance of the transient now and the misidentification of the anisotropy of physical time with a "forward flow of the river of time" vitiates a good deal of philosophical work on time. This work takes as its point of departure the conceptual commitments of the prescientific temporal discourse of common sense in which the "now" of conscious experience is enshrined. Thus, it was none other than the false assumption that coming into being or "flux" must be a feature of physical no less than of psychological (common-sense) time that inspired Henri Bergson's misconceived polemic against the mathematical treatment of motion, which he charged with having erroneously *spatialized* time by a description which leaves out the flux of becoming and renders only the "static" relations of earlier and later. Furthermore, as we shall now see, P. W. Bridgman's critique of A. S. Eddington's thermodynamic account of the anisotropy of time is rendered nugatory by Bridgman's erroneous application of the concept of "unidirectional forward flow" of psychological time to physical time. A statement of our grounds for rejecting Bridgman's critique as unjustified will be instructive even though Eddington's account is open to objections on grounds *other than* those given by Bridgman. Specifically, in the context of time periods sufficiently long to permit the occurrence of Poincaré-Zermelo cycles, the long-term entropic behavior of a closed system obeying the laws of statistical mechanics is completely time-symmetrical. And in that context, one can no longer assume with Eddington that the higher of two entropy states must be the later of the two.

Bridgman contends that the entropy increase cannot be regarded with Eddington as the fundamental indicator of the relation "later than." Speaking of the significance which Bridgman believes Eddington to have ascribed to the invariance of the laws of mechanics under time reversal, Bridgman states his objection to Eddington as follows:[7]

> The significance that Eddington ascribes to it is that the equation is unaffected by a reversal of the direction of flow of time, which would mean that the corresponding physical occurrence is the same whether time flows forward or backward, and his thesis is that in general there is nothing in ordinary mechanical occurrences to indicate whether time is flowing forward or backward. In thermodynamic systems on the other hand, in which entropy increases with time, time enters the differential equation as the first derivative, so that the direction of flow of time cannot be changed without changing the equation. This is taken to indicate that in a thermodynamic system time must flow forward, while it might flow backward in a mechanical system.
>
> . . . How would one go to work in any concrete case to decide whether time were flowing forward or backward? If it were found that the entropy of the

universe were decreasing, would one say that time was flowing backward, or would one say that it was a law of nature that entropy decreases with time? It seems to me that in any operational view of the meaning of natural concepts the notion of time must be used as a primitive concept, which cannot be analyzed, and which can only be accepted, so that it is meaningless to speak of a reversal of the direction of time. I see no way of formulating the underlying operations without assuming as understood the notion of earlier or later in time.

We see that Bridgman takes Eddington to have offered an entropic basis of the "forward flow" of psychological time rather than of the anisotropy of physical time, because Bridgman falsely identifies these two different concepts. And we shall now show that his purported *reductio ad absurdum* argument against Eddington derives its plausibility, but also its lack of cogency, from the conjunction of precisely this illegitimate identification with a contrary-to-fact assumption. Thus, we ask Bridgman: Under what circumstances could it be found that the entropy of the universe "were decreasing"? Bridgman (*ibid.*, pp. 169, 175–177, 181–182) has explicitly rejected as unfounded the conclusion of statistical mechanics that the entropy of a closed system will *decrease* markedly after the system has been in equilibrium for a very long time. For he rejects as gratuitous the assumption that the micro-constituents of thermodynamic systems can be held to behave reversibly in accord with time-symmetric laws whose observational foundation is only macroscopic. Hence Bridgman's hypothetical finding of an entropy *decrease* is predicated on an actual human observation of an overall entropy decrease with increasing psychological time. Thus the situation envisioned by Bridgman would arise in the contrary-to-fact eventuality that physical systems or the universe would exhibit *lower* entropy states at times which are *psychologically later*, and *higher* entropy states at times which are *psychologically earlier*. To appreciate the import of this contrary-to-fact assumption, we note that an experience *B* is *psychologically later* than an experience *A* under one of the following two conditions: (1) the awareness-and-memory content constituting experience *A* is a *proper part* of the memory content of experience *B*, or (2) experience *B* contains the memory of *the fact* of the occurrence of another experience *A* (for instance, the fact of having dreamt), but the memories ingredient in *B* do *not* contain the *content* of experience *A* (for instance, the details of the dream having been forgotten).[8] Thus, psychologically later times are either times at which we do, in fact, have more memories or information than at the correspondingly earlier ones, or they are times at which it would be possible to have a richer store of memories even if the latter did not, in fact, materialize because of partial forgetting. Accordingly, Bridgman's posit of our finding that the entropy "were decreasing" would require the entropy increase among physical systems and the future direction of psychological time to be *temporally counterdirected* as follows: temporally, the direction of increasing entropy among *physical* systems would *not also* be the direction of actual or possible *memory* (information) increase among *biological* organisms, since (actually or possibly) "*richer*" memory states would be coinciding temporally with *lower* entropy states of physical systems. It is to be understood that Bridgman is here positing entropy decreases in those quasi-closed systems which normally increase their entropy, e.g. bathtubs.

What is the logical force of Bridgman's contrary-to-fact assumption as a basis for invalidating Eddington's account of the anisotropy of physical time? Bridgman's objection is seen to be devoid of cogency in the light of the following reasons. In the first place, quite apart from the fact that Eddington was not concerned to account for the "forward flow" of psychological time, *in actual fact* the very production of memories in biological organisms *is causally coupled* to entropy *increases* in certain portions of the external environment. And since Eddington was offering his criterion as an account of what does, in fact, obtain, the adequacy of this account cannot be impugned by the contrary-to-fact logical possibility of counterdirectedness envisioned by Bridgman. But even if the situation posited by Bridgman were to materialize in actuality, it would certainly *not* refute Eddington's claim that (1) the entropic behavior of physical systems renders the opposite directions of physical time anisotropic *on the assumption that the entropy of each of these systems decreases in the one direction and increases in the other* with the possible exception of systems which are essentially in equilibrium throughout their careers, and (2) the direction of increasing entropy can be called the direction of "later than" or time increase. Although Eddington had left himself open to being misunderstood by using the potentially misleading term "time's arrow," he had also sought to spike the misunderstanding that entropically characterized physical time "is flowing forward" in the sense of there being a physical coming into being or becoming.[9]

Contrary to Bridgman, Eddington did *not* think that irreversible processes were needed to assure that physical time would flow forward rather than backward. *Physically*, certain states are later than others by certain amounts of time. But there is no forward "flow" of *physical* time, because purely physically the anthropocentric *now* on whose transiency the flow depends does not exist. Moreover, as applied to *psychological* time, the locution "flow backward" is self-contradictory, since the assertion that the now shifts forward (in the future direction) is a tautology, as we saw. A fluid can flow *spatially* up or down, because the meaning of spatial "flow" is *independent* of the meaning of "spatially up" or "down." But as applied to psychological time, the meaning of the action-verb metaphor "flow" *involves* the meaning of the metaphor "forward," that is, of "from earlier to later." For the *flowing* here denotes metaphorically the shifting of the "now" from earlier to later or "forward." Hence if Bridgman's hypothetical situation of counterdirectedness could actually materialize, we would say that the entropy is decreasing with increasing psychological time without damage to Eddington's account and *not* that time is "flowing backward."

§3. *The Role of Boundary Conditions in Both Thermodynamic and Nonthermodynamic Irreversibility*

There is both a weak sense and a strong sense in which a process might be claimed to be "irreversible" within the framework of a physical theory that allows a sharp distinction between laws and boundary conditions. The weak sense is that the *temporal inverse* of the process in fact never (or hardly ever) occurs with increasing time for the following reason: Certain boundary or initial conditions obtaining in the universe independently of any law (or laws) combine with a relevant law (or laws) to render the temporal inverse *de facto* nonexistent or unreversed, although no law or combination of laws itself disallows that inverse process. The strong sense of "irreversible" is that the temporal inverse is impossible in virtue of being ruled out by a law alone or by a combination of laws. Since the weaker kind of irreversibility arises from boundary conditions which are *contingent* with respect to the laws of nature, I shall refer to the weaker kind of irreversibility as "contingent." And it will turn out that within the framework of the class of physical theories that I shall consider, both the thermodynamic and the nonthermodynamic species of irreversibility yielded by these theories are of *contingent* character rather than vouchsafed by laws.

The complete time symmetry of the basic laws like those of dynamics is entirely compatible with the existence of contingent irreversibility (unreversedness). In the concise and apt words of Penrose and Percival, the reason for this compatibility is that "dynamics relates the states of a system at two different times, but it puts no restriction whatever on the state at any one time, nor on the probability distribution at any one time."[10]

We shall now find that finite thermodynamic systems which are closed for only relatively *short* time periods exhibit an entropy behavior which is contingently statistically irreversible. After considering this type of thermodynamic irreversibility, we shall consider contingently irreversible processes occurring in a spatially infinite universe for which no Boltzmann entropy is defined.

H. Reichenbach has given a detailed discussion of the kind of thermodynamic irreversibility which we are about to consider.[11] But since I believe that Reichenbach's treatment requires significant modification in order to be satisfactory, I shall now set forth what I believe to be a corrected elaboration of his main conception.

Reichenbach points out that there are subsystems which branch off from the wider solar system, galactic system, or from other portions of the universe, remain quasi-closed for a *limited* period of time, and then merge again with the wider system from which they had been separated. And he uses the term "branch-system" to designate this kind of subsystem.[12] Branch-systems are formed not only in the natural course of things, but also through human intervention, such as when an ice cube is placed into a glass of warm gingerale by a waiter and then covered for hygienic purposes until it merges with the wider universe by being consumed by a person. Most but not all branch-systems branch off in initial states of relatively low entropy which are the products of their earlier coupling or interaction with outside agencies of one kind or another. This rather constant and ubiquitous formation of a branch-system in a relatively low-entropy state resulting from interaction often proceeds at the expense of an entropy increase in some wider quasi-closed system from which it originated. And the *de facto*

occurrence of these branch-systems, which is contingent with respect
to the laws of nature, has the following *fundamental consequence*, at
least for our region of the universe and during the current epoch:
among the quasi-closed systems whose entropy is relatively low and
which behave as if they might remain isolated, the vast majority have
not been and will not remain permanently-closed systems, being
branch-systems instead.

Hence, upon encountering a quasi-closed system in a state of fairly
low entropy, we know the following to be overwhelmingly probable:
the system has *not* been isolated for millions and millions of years and
does *not* just *happen* to be in one of the infrequent but ever-recurring
low-entropy states exhibited by a permanently-isolated system. Instead, our system was formed not too long ago by branching off after
an interaction with an outside agency.

Branch systems have a property which has the character of a *bound-*
ary condition in the context of (course-grained) classical statistical
mechanics and which enters into the temporally asymmetrical statistical regularities which we shall find to be exhibited in the entropic
behavior of these systems. This property consists in the following
randomness obtaining *as a matter of contingent fact* in the distribution
of the W_1 microstates belonging to the initial macrostates of a *space*
ensemble of branch-systems, each of which has the same initial entropy
$S_1 = k \log W_1$: for each class of *like* branch-systems having the *same*
initial entropy value S_1, the microstates constituting the identical initial
macrostates of entropy S_1 are *random samples* of the set of all W_1
microstates yielding a macrostate of entropy S_1.[13] This attribute of
randomness of microstates on the part of the initial states of the members of the space ensemble will be recognized as the counterpart of the
following attribute of the microstates of one single, permanently closed
system: there is equiprobability of occurrence among the W_1 microstates belonging to the *time* ensemble of states of equal entropy
$S_1 = k \log W_1$ exhibited by one single, permanently-closed system.

We can now state the statistical regularities which obtain as a consequence of the *de facto* contingent properties of branch systems just set
forth, when coupled with the principles of statistical mechanics. These
regularities, which will be seen to yield a temporally asymmetric statistical behavior of the entropy of branch-systems, fall into two main
groups as follows.

Group 1. In most space ensembles of quasi-closed branch-systems, each of which is initially in a state of nonequilibrium or relatively *low* entropy, the majority of branch-systems in the ensemble will have *higher* entropies *after* a given time t.[14] But these branch-systems simply did not exist as quasi-closed, distinct systems at a time t *prior to* the occurrence of their initial, branching-off states. Hence, not existing then as such, the branch-systems did in fact *not* also exhibit the same higher entropy states at the *earlier* times t, which they would indeed have done then had they existed as closed systems all along.

The increase after a time t in the entropy of the overwhelming majority of branch-systems of initially low entropy —as confirmed abundantly by observation—can be made fully intelligible. To do so, we note the following property of the *time* ensemble of entropy values belonging to a single, permanently-closed system and then affirm that property of the space ensembles of branch-systems: since *large* entropic downgrades or decreases are *far less* probable (frequent) than moderate ones, the *vast majority* of *non*equilibrium entropy states of a permanently-closed system are located either at or in the immediate temporal vicinity of the *bottom* of a *dip* of the one-system entropy curve. In short, the vast majority of the *sub*maximum entropy states are on or temporally very near the *upgrades* of the one-system curve. The application of this result to the space ensemble of branch-systems whose initial states exhibit the aforementioned *de facto* property of randomness then yields the following: among the initial low entropy states of these systems, the vast majority lie at or in the immediate temporal vicinity of the bottoms of the one-system entropy curve at which an upgrade begins.

Group 2. A decisive *temporal asymmetry* in the statistics of the temporal evolution of branch-systems arises from the further result that in most space ensembles of branch-systems each of whose members is initially in a state of *equilibrium* or very *high* entropy (for example, a covered glass of lukewarm water just drawn from a reservoir of water at the same uniform temperature), the vast majority of these systems in the ensemble will *not* have *lower* entropies *after* a finite time t, but will still be in equilibrium.[15] For the aforementioned randomness property assures that the vast majority of those branch-systems whose initial states are equilibrium states have maximum entropy values lying somewhere *well within* the plateau of the one-system entropy curve, rather than at the extremity of the plateau at which an entropy *decrease* is initiated.[16]

We see therefore that, in the vast majority of branch-systems, either one end of their finite entropy curves is a point of low entropy and the other a point of high entropy, or they are in equilibrium states at both ends as well as during the intervening interval. And it is likewise apparent that the statistical distribution of these entropy values on the time axis is such that the vast majority of branch-systems have the *same direction of entropy increase* and hence also the same opposite direction of entropy decrease. Thus, the statistics of entropy increase among branch-systems assures that in most space ensembles the vast majority of branch-systems will increase their entropy in *one* of the two opposite time directions and decrease it in the other. In this way, *the entropic behavior of branch-systems confers the same statistical anisotropy on the vast majority of all those epochs of time during which the universe exhibits the requisite disequilibrium and contains branch-systems satisfying initial conditions of "randomness."*

Let us now call the direction of entropy increase of a typical representative of these epochs the direction of "later," as indeed we have done from the outset by the mere assignment of higher time numbers in that direction, but without prejudice to our findings concerning the issue of the anisotropy of time. Then our results pertaining to the entropic behavior of branch-systems show that the directions of "earlier than" and "later than" are not merely opposite directions bearing decreasing and increasing time coordinates respectively, but are statistically *anisotropic* in an objective physical sense. This statistical anisotropy is an objective *macroscopic* fact even though the behavior of the entropy function as a mathematical entity depends on human choices as to the size of the cells in phase space.

As we just saw, the entropic statistical anisotropy of time can be described without having to characterize the direction of entropy increase as the direction of increasing time coordinates. Thus, this anisotropy surely does not depend on our assigning the lower of two time coordinates t_1 and t_2 to the lower of two entropy states of a branch-system. Nor is that anisotropy implicit in designating the lower of these two states as the "initial" state rather than as the "final" state, a designation which results from the customary coordinatization of the time continuum. Using either the usual time coordinatization or one obtained from it via the transformation $t \rightarrow -t$, we are able to assert that for each branch-system there is a finite time interval $t_1 \leq t \leq t_2$ to which its existence is confined. And if the boundary conditions governing the branch-systems are specified for *either one* of the extremities of their finite careers, then the one-system entropy curve yields both the states of these systems at their other extremities and their behavior during the intervening time. Let us now utilize the latter fact to clarify our results further by showing the following: the same entropic statistical anisotropy of time results *both* from the boundary conditions governing the initial states at time t_1 *and* also from those pertaining to the final states at time t_2.

If we use the language of the usual time coordinatization, we can assert that during a cosmic epoch of disequilibrium, the following is a *de facto* property of a typical space ensemble of branch-systems which form at a given time t_1: a good many of its members are in relatively low entropy states at the given time t_1 ("subclass A"), while others are in essentially equilibrium states at that time ("subclass B"). On the strength of the aforementioned randomness of the initial states at t_1, at the time t_2 $(t_2 > t_1)$, the existing A-systems and B-systems are in entropy states as follows: higher states of the A systems at time t_2 lie temporally near or at the near *extremity of a plateau* of the one-system curve, whereas the equilibrium states of the B-systems prevailing at time t_2 lie *well within a plateau* of the one-system curve. Again using the language of the usual time coordinatization, the boundary conditions can be given *alternatively* for the time t_2 by the following compound specification. (1) At time t_2, there exist branch-systems (of type A) which are in relatively high entropy states lying temporally very near or at the extremity of a plateau of the one-system curve—hence the microstates underlying these high entropy states of the A-systems are *not* random (typical) samples of the totality of microstates, each one of which constitutes a macrostate of the same high entropy; and (2) at time t_2, there also exist branch-systems (of type B) which are in equilibrium states lying well within a plateau of the one-system curve—hence the microstates underlying the equilibrium states of these B-systems are indeed random (typical) samples of the totality of microstates, each one of which constitutes an equilibrium state of the same entropy. But if we are thus given that at the time t_2 branch-systems of types A and B exist in high entropy states *as specified*, then the one-system entropy curve tells us that the A-systems *decrease* their entropies in the direction of time t_1 while the B-systems maintain equilibrium states in that direction. For this curve shows us that the "nonrandom" high states of the A-systems at time t_2 evolved from lower ones at time t_1, whereas the "random" equilibrium states of the B-systems at time t_2 came from like equilibrium states prevailing throughout their careers. It is now clear that if the boundary conditions are correctly specified for *either one* of the two ends of the careers of the branch-systems, the otherwise time-symmetrical one-system entropy curve yields a statistical anisotropy of time. And it is further evident that the same conclusion would have been reached, if the *de facto* obtaining boundary conditions had been correspondingly codified in a time language based on replacing the usual time coordinatization according to the transformation $t \to -t$. It has been understood in this discussion that branch-systems do *not* exist long enough as such to endure for a period comparable to that of a typical entropy plateau of the one-system curve.

It should be noted that I have characterized the positive direction of time as the direction of entropy increase for a *typical representative* of all those epochs of time during which the universe exhibits the requisite disequilibrium and contains branch-systems satisfying initial conditions of "randomness." Accordingly, it is entirely possible and consistent to speak of the *atypically* behaving branch-systems, whose entropy increases are *counterdirected* with respect to those of the majority, as *decreasing* their entropies in the positive direction of time. Since we are able to give the usual temporal description of fluctuation phenomena in this way, we must therefore wholly reject the following argument by Karl Popper, which he offered in an endeavor to show that thermodynamic phenomena cannot constitute a physical basis for the anisotropy of time:

> The suggestion has been made (first by Boltzmann himself) that the arrow of time is, either by its very nature, or by definition, connected with the increase in entropy; so that entropy cannot decrease in time because a decrease would mean a reversal of its arrow, and therefore an increase relative to the reversed arrow. Much as I admire the boldness of this idea, I think that it is absurd, especially in view of the undeniable fact that thermodynamic fluctuations do exist. One would have to assert that, within the spatial region of the fluctuation, all clocks run backwards if seen from outside that region. But this assertion would destroy that very system of dynamics on which the statistical theory is founded. (Moreover, most clocks are non-entropic systems, in the sense that their heat production, far from being essential to their function, is inimical to it.)
>
> I do not believe that Boltzmann would have made his suggestion after 1905, when fluctuations, previously considered no more than mathematically calculable near-impossibilities, suddenly became the strongest evidence in favour of the

physical reality of molecules. (I am alluding to Einstein's theory of Brownian motion.) As it is, a statistical theory of the arrow of time seems to me unacceptable.[17]

More recently, Popper [*Nature*, **207** (1965), 233–234] has presented the following further arguments in an endeavor to show that the statistics of thermodynamic phenomena cannot be validly regarded as a physical foundation for the anisotropy of time:

... we can split the change of entropy dS_X in any system X into two parts: dS_{X_e}, or the flow of entropy due to interaction with the exterior of X, and dS_{X_i}, the contribution to the change of entropy due to changes inside the system X. We have of course:

$$dS_X = dS_{X_e} + dS_{X_i} \qquad (1)$$

and we can express the second law by:

$$dS_{X_i} \geq 0, \qquad (2)$$

For an energetically closed (or "isolated") system X, for which by definition $dS_{X_e} = 0$, expression (2) formulates the classical statement that entropy never decreases. But if X is open towards a cooler exterior:

$$dS_{X_e} < 0 \qquad (3)$$

holds, and the question whether its total entropy increases or decreases depends, of course, on both its entropy production dS_{X_i} and its entropy loss dS_{X_e}.

... With very few and short-lived exceptions, the entropy in almost all known regions (of sufficient size) of our universe either remains constant or decreases, although energy is dissipated (by escaping from the system in question).

... in almost all sufficiently large systems known to us, entropy production seems to be equalled, or even exceeded, by entropy loss through heat radiation. . . .

So there do not seem to be theoretical or empirical reasons to attribute to expression (2) any cosmic significance or to connect 'time's arrow' with that expression; especially since the equality sign in expression (2) may hold for almost all cosmical regions (and especially for regions empty of matter). Moreover, we have good reason to interpret expression (2) as a statistical law; while the 'arrow' of time, or the 'flow' of time, does not seem to be of a stochastic character: nothing suggests that it is subject to statistical fluctuation, or connected with a law of large numbers.

These further arguments by Popper do not prove convincing for the following reasons:

1. Most of the systems which we encounter in our physical environment and whose (thermodynamic) behavior we observe are *not* Popper's

"sufficiently large systems" (for example, our solar system, known stars) for which dS_X is zero or even negative; instead, they are systems for which $dS_X = dS_{X_i}$ to a fairly good approximation and which qualify as branch systems in Reichenbach's sense (for example, mixing processes such as hot and cold water forming a lukewarm mixture, wood burning in a fireplace, floating ice melting in a lake). Hence the failure of dS_X to be positive in the minority case of "sufficiently large systems" cannot detract from the fact that for the majority of the relevant systems, the total entropy change dS_X is indeed adequately rendered by equation (2). Thus, while there is an interesting sense in which the existence of Popper's sufficiently large systems erodes the "cosmic significance" of equation (2), he is apparently not entitled to his conclusion that there is no reason to connect time's arrow with that equation.

2. When Popper declares that "the 'arrow' of time . . . does not seem to be of a stochastic character," one must ask what context of experience or presumed fact he is invoking in support of this statement. Surely the daily experiences of life as conceptualized in common sense are not competent to yield a verdict on the stochasticity of those physical features of the world which are presumed to constitute the foundations for the observed "arrow."

I have contended against Popper that the entropic behavior of branch systems confers the *same* statistical anisotropy on the vast majority of all those cosmic epochs of time during which the universe exhibits the requisite disequilibrium and contains branch-systems satisfying the specified initial conditions of "randomness." My conclusion that the *same* statistical anisotropy pervasively characterizes the overwhelming majority of the cosmic epochs of disequilibrium is supported by the findings of Penrose and Percival, who reject Boltzmann's contrary view on the basis of their Law of Conditional Independence.[18] But my claim of statistical anisotropy departs significantly from Reichenbach's "hypothesis of the branch structure"[19] in two ways. (1) Since the universe may be spatially infinite, I do *not* assume with Reichenbach that the entropy is defined for the entire universe such that the universe as a whole can be presumed to exhibit the entropic evolution of the statistical entropy curve for a permanently closed, *finite* system. Therefore (2) I do *not* conclude, as Reichenbach does, that there is a parallelism of the direction of entropy increase of the universe and of the branch-systems at any time, such that cosmically the statistical anisotropy of time is only local by "fluctuating" in the sense that the supposed alternations of epochs of entropy increase and decrease of the universe go hand in hand with the alleged alternations of the direction of entropy increase in the ensembles of branch systems associated with these respective epochs, successive disequilibrium epochs allegedly being entropically *counterdirected* with respect to each other.

In view of the reservations which Reichenbach himself expressed[20] concerning the reliability of assumptions regarding the universe as a whole in the present state of cosmology, one wonders why he invoked the *entropy* of the universe at all instead of confining himself, as I have done, to the much weaker assumption of the existence of states of disequilibrium in the universe. More fundamentally, it is unclear how Reichenbach thought he could reconcile the assumption that the branch-systems satisfy initial conditions of randomness during whatever cosmic epoch they may form—an assumption which, as we saw, makes for the *same* statistical anisotropy on the part of *most* disequilibrium epochs of the universe—with his claim of alternation: "When we come to the downgrade [of the entropy curve of the entire universe], always proceeding in the same direction [along the time axis], the branches begin at states of high entropy, . . . and they end at points of low entropy."[21] Contrary to Reichenbach, we saw in our statement of the consequences of the postulate of randomness under Group 2 above that, in the vast majority of cases, branch-systems beginning in a state of equilibrium (high entropy) will *remain* in equilibrium for the duration of their finite careers instead of decreasing their entropies!

An inherent limitation on the applicability of the Maxwell-Boltzmann entropy concept to the entire universe lies in the fact that it has no applicability at all to a *spatially infinite* universe for the following reasons. If the infinite universe contains a denumerable *infinity* of atoms, molecules, or stars, the number of complexions W becomes undefined or infinite, so that the entropy is not defined, and *a fortiori* no increase or decrease thereof.[22] And if the number of particles in the infinite universe is only finite, then (a) the equilibrium state of maximum entropy cannot be realized by a *finite* number of particles in a phase space of *infinitely* many cells, since these particles would have to be *uniformly* distributed among these cells, and (b) the quasi-ergodic hypothesis, which provides the essential basis for the probability metric ingredient in the Maxwell-Boltzmann entropy concept, is presumably false for an infinite phase space.[23]

If the universe *were finite and* such that an entropy is defined for it as a whole which conforms to the one-system entropy curve of statistical mechanics, then my contention of a *cosmically pervasive statistical anisotropy* of time could no longer be upheld. For I am assuming that the vast majority of branch-systems in most epochs increase their entropy in the same direction and that space ensembles of branch-systems do form during most periods of disequilibrium. And if one may further assume that the entropy of a finite, spatially closed universe depends *additively* on the entropies of its component subsystems, then the assumed temporal asymmetry of the entropy behavior of the branch-systems would appear to contradict the complete *time symmetry* of the one-system entropy behavior of the finite universe. This conclusion, if correct, therefore poses the question—which I merely wish to ask here—whether in a closed universe the postulate of the randomness of the initial conditions would not hold. For in that case, the cosmically *pervasive* statistical anisotropy of time which is assured by the randomness postulate would not obtain; instead, one could then assume initial conditions in branch-systems that issue in Reichenbach's cosmically local kind of anisotropy of time, successive overall disequilibrium epochs having *opposite* directions of entropy increase both in the universe and in the branch-systems associated with these epochs.

Our conclusions regarding the entropy statistics of branch-systems can now be used to elucidate the conditions under which retrodiction of the past is feasible while corresponding prediction of the future is not.

Suppose we encounter a beach whose sand forms a smooth surface except for one place where it is in the shape of a human footprint. We know from our previous considerations with high probability that instead of having evolved *isolatedly* from a prior state of uniform smoothness into its present uneven configuration according to the statistical entropy principle for a permanently closed system, the beach was an *open* system in *interaction* with a stroller. And we are aware furthermore that if there is some quasi-closed wider system containing the beach and the stroller, as there often is, the beach achieved its ordered low entropy state of bearing the imprint or interaction indicator at the expense of an at least compensatory entropy increase in that wider system comprising the stroller; the stroller increased the entropy of the wider system by scattering his energy reserves in making the footprint.

Thus the sandy footprint shape is a genuine indicator and not a randomly achieved form resulting from the unperturbed chance concatenations of the grains of sand. The imprint thus contains information in the sense of being a veridical indicator of an interaction. Now, in all probability the entropy of the imprint-bearing beach system increases after the interaction with the stroller through the smoothing action of the wind. And this entropy increase is parallel, in all probability, to the direction of entropy increase of the majority of branch-systems. Moreover, we saw that the production of the indicator by the interaction is likely to have involved an entropy increase in some wider system of which the indicator is a part. Hence, *in all probability the states of the interacting systems which do contain the indicators of the interaction are the relatively higher entropy states of the majority of branch-systems, as compared to the interaction state. Hence the indicator states are the relatively later states as compared to the states of interaction which they attest.* And by being both *later* and indicators, these states have *retrodictive* significance, thereby being traces, records, or "memories." And due to the high degree of retrodictive univocity of the low-entropy states constituting the indicators, the latter are veridical to a high degree of *specificity*, although that univocity does not derive from their low entropy alone.

Confining our attention to indicators *whose production requires only the occurrence of the interaction which they attest*, we therefore obtain the following conclusion. Apart from some kinds of *advance* indicators requiring very special conditions for their production and constituting *exceptions*, it is the case that, *with overwhelming probability, low entropy indicator states can exist in systems whose interactions they attest only after and not before these interactions.*

Two of these exceptions, which I have discussed elsewhere in some detail,[24] are constituted by the following two classes of advance indicators: (1) veridical predictions made and stored (recorded) by human (or other thinking, theory-using) beings, and physically registered, bona fide advance indicators produced by computers, and (2) advance indicators (for instance, sudden barometric drops) which are produced by the very cause (pressure change) that also produces the future interaction (storm) indicated by them.

Hence, the two or more exceptions apart, we arrive at the fundamental asymmetry of recordability: *reliable indicators in interacting*

systems permit only retrodictive inferences concerning the interactions
for which they vouch but no predictive inferences pertaining to corre-
sponding later interactions.

In the thermodynamic context which we have been considering, there is also the *converse* temporal asymmetry of inferribility, allowing the prediction of state s_2 on the basis of state s_1 but *not* the retrodiction of s_1 from s_2. The latter asymmetry obtains under the following kinds of conditions. In the case of a nonequilibrium system whose temperature behavior is governed by the diffusion equation, the entropy increases with time, and we can predict that the existing nonequilibrium state will tend toward equilibrium. But if the system is in equilibrium to start with, then the temperature information furnished by the diffusion equation does not permit us to retrodict the particular sequence of nonequilibrium temperature distributions which issued in the present equilibrium, since no such sequence is unique.[25]

Another illustration of the same temporal asymmetry of inferribility in equilibrating processes is given by the case of a ball rolling down the wall on the inside of a round bowl subject to friction. If the ball is found to be at rest at the bottom of the bowl, we *cannot retrodict* its particular motion prior to coming to rest, but if the ball is released at the inside wall near the top, we *can* predict its subsequent coming to rest at the bottom.

§4. *Nonthermodynamic Contingent Irreversibility*

Processes characterized by temporally asymmetric entropy changes are not the sole source of the anisotropy of time. That there are physical processes which are *contingently* irreversible independently of any involvement of any Boltzmannian entropy increase was emphasized by K. R. Popper in a series of four notes in *Nature*, which appeared during the years 1956–1958.[26] Popper mentions a suggestion to this effect made by Einstein in 1910. In response to the first two of Popper's four notes, E. L. Hill and I published a communication in *Nature* in 1957[27] in which we endorsed the substance of Popper's claim that there is nonthermodynamic contingent irreversibility in nature, though we generalized Popper's formulation so as to obviate an objection to it. And in their joint paper of 1962 on "The Direction of Time,"[28] Penrose and Percival independently introduced the core idea underlying the generalization set forth by Hill and myself. Specifically, they derive their fundamental principle of temporal asymmetry or "law of conditional independence" from the assumption that "the causal influences coming from infinity in different directions are independent."

In the first three of Popper's four notes, he points to the existence of processes whose temporal inverses are allowed by the *laws* governing elementary processes, but which are contingently *irreversible* for the following reason: the *spontaneous* concatenation of the initial conditions requisite for the occurrence of their temporal inverses is well-nigh physically nonexistent. And the contingent irreversibility of these processes does *not depend* on any involvement of a Boltzmannian entropy increase even when such an entropy increase is actually superposed.

Specifically, independently of O. Costa de Beauregard, who had used the same illustration before him,[29] Popper (I) considers a large surface of water initially at rest into which a stone is dropped, thereby producing an outgoing wave of decreasing amplitude spreading concentrically about the point of the stone's impact. And Popper argues that this process is irreversible in the sense that the "spontaneous" (IV) concatenation on all points of a circle of the initial conditions requisite to the occurrence of a corresponding *contracting* wave is physically impossible, a "spontaneous" concatenation being understood to be one which is *not* brought about by coordinated influences emanating from a common center. Being predicated on the latter spontaneity, this contingent irreversibility is of a *conditional* kind. We see that Popper rightly adduces the need for the *coherence* of the initial conditions as his basis for denying the possibility of their *spontaneous* concatenation. Says he (III): "Only such conditions can be causally realized as can be organized from one centre . . . . Causes which are not centrally correlated are causally unrelated, and can cooperate [that is, produce coherence in the form of *isotropic* contraction of waves to a precise point] only by accident. . . . The probability of such an accident will be zero."

Since the irreversibility of the processes discussed by Popper is conditional on the *spontaneity* of the initial conditions requisite to the occurrence of their temporal inverses, the 1957 paper by E. L. Hill and myself presented a revised form of Popper's claim dispensing with his proviso of spontaneity. Specifically, Hill and I were mindful of the role of the *infinitude* or *"openness"* of a physical system (the universe)—as opposed to the finitude of *closed* systems—in rendering Popper's spontaneity proviso dispensable. Hence Hill and I[30] made the following existential claim concerning processes in "open" (infinite) systems whose irreversibility is *non*entropic and *de facto:*

In classical mechanics the closed systems have quasi-periodic orbits, whereas the open systems have at least some aperiodic orbits which extend to infinity. . . . There exists a fundamental distinction between the two kinds of system in the following sense. In open systems there always exists a class of allowed elementary processes the inverses of which are unacceptable on physical grounds by requiring a *deus ex machina* for their production. For example, in an open universe, matter or radiation can travel away indefinitely from the "finite" region of space, and so be permanently lost. The inverse process would require matter or radiant energy coming from "infinity," and so would involve a process which is not realizable by physical sources. Einstein's example of an outgoing light wave and Popper's analogous case of a water wave are special finite illustrations of this principle.

As a further example, we note that though *allowed* by the *laws* of mechanics, there seem to exist no "implosions" at all which would qualify as the temporal inverses of eternally progressing "explosions" of very thin gases from a center into infinite space. In the light of this fact, one can assert the *de facto* irreversibility of an eternal "explosion" *unconditionally*, that is, *without* Popper's restrictive proviso of *spontaneity* in regard to the production of the *coherent* initial conditions requisite for its inverse. For in an infinite space, there is even no possibility at all of a *non*spontaneous production of the coherent "initial" conditions for an implosion having the following properties: the gas particles converge to a point after having been moving through infinite space for all past eternity in a manner constituting the temporal inverse of the expansion of a very thin gas from a point for all future eternity. There can be no question of a *non*spontaneous realization of the "initial" conditions required for the latter kind of implosion, since such a realization would involve a self-contradictory condition akin to that in Kant's fallacious First Antinomy: the requirement that a process which has been going on for all infinite past time must have had a finite beginning (production by past *initial* conditions) after all.

On the other hand, in a spatially *finite* system it is indeed possible to produce *non*spontaneously the initial conditions for contracting waves and for implosions of gas particles which converge to a point. Thus, assuming negligible viscosity, there are expanding water waves in *finite* systems of which the temporal inverses could be produced *non-*

spontaneously by dropping a very large circular object onto the water surface so that all parts of the circular object strike the water surface simultaneously. And hence there are conditions under which contracting waves do exist in finite systems. But there is no need whatever for Popper's spontaneity proviso to assert the *de facto* irreversibility of the eternal expansion of a *spherical light wave* from a center through infinite space! If space is infinite, the existence of the latter process of expansion is assured by the facts of observation in conjunction with electromagnetic theory; but despite the fact that the *laws* for a homogeneous and isotropic medium *allow* the *inverse* process no less than the actual one,[31] we never encounter the inverse process of spherical waves closing in isotropically to a sharp point of extinction.

It will be noted that Hill and I spoke of there being "at least some aperiodic orbits which extend to infinity" in the classical mechanics of open systems. Thus we were careful *not* to assert that *every* such allowed process extending to infinity is a *de facto* irreversible one, a fact which was unfortunately overlooked by both Popper and H. Mehlberg in their published objections to our note.[32] Instead of making the sweeping assertion which these authors erroneously imputed to us, we affirmed the existence of a *de facto* irreversibility which is *not* predicated on Popper's spontaneity proviso by saying that "there always exists a class of allowed elementary processes" which are thus *de facto* irreversible. And, for my part, I conceived of this claim as constituting an extension of Popper's recognition of the essential role of *coherence* in *de facto* irreversibility to processes of the following kind: processes whose *de facto* irreversibility is *not* conditional on Popper's finitist requirement of spontaneity, because these processes extend to "infinity" in open systems and would hence have inverses in which matter or energy would have to come from "infinity" *coherently* so as to converge upon a point.

Hill and I also pointed out that the contingent irreversibility of the spatially symmetrical eternal propagation of a pulse of light from a point source into *infinite* space does *not* depend on whether the light pulse is undulatory instead of being constituted by a swarm of photons. Neither does *this* irreversibility depend on the acceptance of the steady-state theory of cosmology which, in the words of T. Gold,[33] offers the following explanation for the fact that the universe is a nonreflecting sink for radiation:

It is this facility of the universe to soak up any amount of radiation that makes it different from any closed box, and it is just this that enables it to define the arrow of time in any system that is in contact with this sink. But why is it that the universe is a non-reflecting sink for radiation? Different explanations are offered for this in the various cosmological theories and in some schemes, indeed, this would only be a temporary property.[34] In the steady state universe it is entirely attributed to the state of expansion. The red shift operates to diminish the contribution to the radiation field of distant matter; even though the density does not diminish at great distances, the sky is dark because in most directions the material on a line of sight is receding very fast.

What Gold appears to have in mind here is that due to a very substantial Doppler shift of the radiation emitted by the receding galaxies, the frequency v becomes very low or goes to zero, and since the energy of that radiation is given by $E=hv$, very little if any is received by us converging from these sources. And he goes on to say:

This photon expansion going on around most material is the most striking type of asymmetry, and it appears to give rise to all other time asymmetries that are in evidence. The preferential divergence, rather than convergence, of the world lines of a system ceases when that system has been isolated in a box which prevents the expansion of the photons out into space. Time's arrow is then lost.

We see that Gold's account includes an appreciation of the decisive role played by the infinitude of the space in rendering irreversible the radiation spreading from a point. To be sure, he does emphasize that the Doppler shift due to the expansion makes for the darkness of the sky at night, which would otherwise be lit up by strong radiation. But the *crucial* point is the following: even if the energy of radiation from receding galaxies were not drastically attenuated by the Doppler shift, such radiation would still *not* be the inverse of a process in which a pulse of photons from a point source *forever* spreads symmetrically into *infinite* space from that point source. The nonexistent inverse of the *latter* process of outgoing radiation would be a contracting configuration of photons that has been coming from "infinity"—in other words, from no sources at all—and has been converging on a point for all *infinite* past time. But I grant that the *observational* significance of the latter contingent irreversibility alone is meager.

In conclusion, I recognize that the scope of the preceding discussion ought to be enlarged to include more detailed allowance for the results of further physical theories such as the steady-state cosmology. With respect to that wider class of physical theories, the connection between the thermodynamic and nonthermodynamic kinds of irreversibility may well turn out to be a good deal deeper than this paper has claimed. Specifically, the connection may go beyond the fact that both kinds of irreversibility are due to boundary conditions rather than to laws and fail to obtain in the case of systems which are both spatially finite and permanently closed. Thus, Gold inseparably links all temporal asymmetries which make for the anisotropy of time with the time asymmetry between the divergence and convergence of the geodesics associated with fundamental observers (expansion of the universe). For he relates the temporal asymmetry in all statistical processes to the tendency for radiation to diverge with positive time, a tendency which he relates, in turn, to the expansion of the universe. Having thus linked the thermodynamic and electromagnetic time asymmetries to a cosmological one, Gold reaches the following conclusion:[35]

Most systems when they are not isolated show a clear sense of time. If they become isolated the arrow of time persists in them for awhile, not definable with complete certainty, but with a probability that decreases from a high value initially to zero eventually. The time scale of the decrease of probability depends upon the details of the system.

This conclusion is entirely in accord with the contention of this paper that irreversibility does *not* characterize the long-term behavior of systems which are both spatially finite and permanently closed, but rather other types of systems.

It is a pleasure to note here my indebtedness to Professor Allen Janis for helpful discussions of the relevance of the randomness assumption to the material of §3.

HOYLE

I am not convinced against the flow of time. If we regard ourselves as four-dimensional structures, then our conscious awareness of the present must be regarded as a subset of events from our whole four-dimensional structure. Now the question is: What rule do we accept for determining that subset? As soon as we take a subset of events from a larger collection, we need some sort of rule to define these events. The rule would give us the meaning of "now," and out of this rule we would expect to understand what is meant by the flow of time. I cannot see any reason why we should disregard our awareness of the present as an invalid experience. In the "present" we go into the laboratory and do an experiment. We look at a photograph of a galaxy that is in the present and we accept this as a valid observation. Why is the rest of the present not an equally valid observation?

ROSENFELD

This is a real problem, but I think it is a problem of human psychology. We are talking of the logical problem of the definition of time.

HOYLE

I would agree that this is a problem of psychology if we can say that every experiment that is done in physics is a question of psychology.

MORRISON

We can translate every question of experiment to a question of memory content, even of computing machines.

GRÜNBAUM

No, because they are not conscious. That is just the point.

MORRISON

But it is easy to make them "conscious" in some degree; then we can argue about the degree. I can give you a computing machine that knows what the "now" is. The "now" machine is a machine that has short- and long-term memories, and it gives the contents of the short-term memory within a tenth of a second as its "now." Content of the memory is everything that it has received. I do not regard this as subjective.

GOLD

Morrison is trying to drive Grünbaum to say: "Ah, but it is also just the same kind of a thing for a human."

GRÜNBAUM

Yes. But I want to say that there is a difference between a conscious thing and an unconscious thing.

X

What is that difference?

GRÜNBAUM

Well, I do not have more precise words in which to say this, but I would not be worried if a computer is unemployed. If a human being is unemployed, I would worry about the sorrows which that human being experiences in virtue of conceptualized self-awareness.

X

Are dogs conscious?

GRÜNBAUM

Well, yes. It is going to be a question of degree. But I wonder whether they have *conceptualized* awareness.

X

Are cockroaches conscious?

GRÜNBAUM

Well, I do not know about the nervous system of the cockroach.

X

Well, they do not suffer from unemployment.

MORRISON

If I make a good enough automaton, you would become sorry when it is unemployed. I do not insist that the computers are conscious by definition; I say only that I see no obstruction to this. Of course I cannot produce consciousness by building a machine that has little "bits" of consciousness out of which eventually real consciousness is constructed. But whatever you would be willing to say about humans you would be willing to say about the machine.

X

I am trying to understand why the feelings of sorrow are vital to the understanding of time. Consciousness is essential to Grünbaum's argument, and consciousness in turn depends upon feeling sorry.

ROBINSON

Supposing I concede that I understand what consciousness is, which as a matter of fact I don't, but this enables me to carry the argument a little further. As I see it, the kind of difficulty we are faced with is that of reconciling the four-dimensional picture that we draw with our feeling of the unfolding of events. Is it possible to reformulate Weyl's idea in some way in which it presents the essential content but is not metaphorical and misleading?

GRÜNBAUM

Yes. In literal form, the thesis which Weyl put forward and which I endorse is just this: when we speak of the "flow of time" or when we speak of "coming into being," we are speaking about something which depends intrinsically on the presence of the conscious awareness for its existence or relevance or meaningfulness. This is not trivial, because "coming into being" has no relevance, for example, to the world before evolution took place, assuming there were no other conscious organisms elsewhere in other galaxies and so on. It is an illuminating point that this is introduced by the perspective of thinking organisms. Now, this remark is not to dismiss "coming into being" as pragmatically irrelevant; this is merely to separate from the description of nature the things which depend on our presence from things which do not.

MORRISON

You mean "on the presence of any system with internal states." I think you are going to be pressed to that pretty soon.

GRÜNBAUM

I do agree that if conceptualized awareness were exhibited by a suitably complicated cybernetic "hardware" device, then such a machine would generate "now"-attributes no less than your mind or mine when registering events. What I claim is that nowness is mind-dependent, *not* that the human organism alone is mind-possessing.

X

The only thing that Grünbaum is really worried about is his *own* consciousness. The existence of other consciousnesses is not sufficient to define this "now" that we have been talking about.

BERGMANN

All I have to do is to make myself understood by the microphone because it is the only one of us that has permanent consciousness.

Aside from this philosophical question of the consciousness, we can, with our present understanding of the nature of space and time, formulate the following question. Assuming that the whole universe is a four-dimensional collection of world points or events, and that this universe can be covered by a congruence of three-dimensional spacelike sets, are there cosmological models in which this can be done and others in which it cannot be done, provided that this understanding of the topological and geometrical nature of the universe should persist through the next stage of theoretical development? This is a meaningful question quite apart from the existence of conscious observers. Now, the reason that we ask this question and think that the answer to it ought to be "yes," is that, in the region of a four-dimensional tube that is in our vicinity, this topological construction can be carried out. That it can be carried out with the whole universe is an entirely different question.

This situation is somewhat analogous to the state of the art at the time of Kant, who claimed that the Newtonian conception of space and time was *a priori* because he was not aware of other logical possibilities. There may be other logical possibilities which are inconsistent with the naïve view of the flow of time.

BONDI

I think that in our psychological comparison of the past and the future, we suffer from the tendency to overestimate our memories as compared with our ability to forecast.

GRÜNBAUM

Is not this reasonably well founded? Obviously there are mistakes in memories, but there is a fairly good correlation between widely held memories and corroborating evidence at different times.

BONDI

But there are many things of which nobody has any memory, things of which no records exist. Yet these things may be relevant for us.

GOLD

All this is only a question of anisotropy as we have discussed it. It does seem necessary to find a rule that gives us this subjective impression of flow. While it seems that we must discuss part of the real world without involving ourselves, we know about it all only from subjective introspection. However, we can make a consistent picture of a real world around us and not just one of consciousness. So far as this apparent flow of time is concerned, we cannot make a distinction between a real world and the subjective world. I think there is that distinction to be made. We ought to eliminate this flow idea from the real picture, but before we can eliminate it we ought to understand how it arises. We should understand that there can be a self-consistent set of rules that would give a beast this kind of a phoney picture of time, and if that set of rules cannot be found, then we cannot order the world into the "external" and "internal."

BONDI

But this set of rules is surely quite simple. To my memory, my various "nows" each contain memories. If a memory contains a memory of the remembering at another instant, then I thereby define the other time as being earlier.

HOYLE

Suppose we define as the "present" the intersection of a four-dimensional tube with a spacelike surface. Then a scalar function of position equals some specified constant, and the value of that constant determines the present. By changing that constant, we get a different set of intersections. So "now" is the meaning attached to the constant. The flow of time is just the one-parameter family of surfaces.

GRÜNBAUM

That is an order structure. You are saying that, in accordance with some arbitrary criterion, any particular section instead of another one is the "now." Of course in that sense the "now" is the same as that used in a Minkowski diagram. This "now" surely can be arbitrarily picked, whereas the "nows" that you consider as "nows" in your life are not arbitrarily picked, because you constitute a particular segment of the career of the universe. A problem about specifying any particular event or sets of events in the world applies not only to the events to which we are witness consciously, but to any sets of events. The question of what happened on the island of Manhattan before any man walked the surface of the earth is a case in point.

BERGMANN

This is the kind of "now" in flow of time that you can settle only by retiring into the corner and not talking to anybody else. If you want to be bothered by this problem you really have to become a solipsist.

X

Grünbaum associates with consciousness the feeling that there is a "now." I believe, however, that it is possible to describe physical events having to do with the connection or correlation of one region of space, such as that inside the brain, with what is on the outside, that is, in other locations on the space-time diagram. This sort of correlation, I believe, would produce in a sufficiently elaborate machine a feeling of "now," an understanding of the past, and so on. Viewing the connection in this way is more objective and does not involve consciousness directly.

GRÜNBAUM

In emphasizing that consciousness imports something into the description of this situation, I do not mean to dissociate its neuro-physiological basis from the rest of physical events. Surely there are physical events in the brain which must be associated with this process. These are not two completely unrelated worlds coming into accidental contiguity with each other.

GOLD

If we do not take as objective reality the progression of the world along the time coordinate, then I can see no harm in the subsystems giving occasionally a wrong definition of time anisotropy because of inadequate statistics, as it were. It is not small subsystems that we are aware of. We do not reverse our apparent sense of time because we are sufficiently big subsystems so that such a deflection never occurs. If we were composed of three atoms or so, then we might be completely crazy! Every now and again we would reverse our relative sense of time. But we are complicated systems. I see no reason for objecting to a purely thermodynamic anisotropy of time, provided we have no separate thing to explain, namely a flow or progression.

GRÜNBAUM

Yes, although Popper would say, I think, that his other basis, viz., the practical absence of the boundary conditions needed for the inverses of certain processes is a more universal one. How he knows this is not quite clear, but perhaps it is independent of those boundary conditions which make for the thermodynamics.

GOLD

But the two are the same thing, surely! It is the boundary conditions that define in which sense the pattern of world lines diverges. All the internal time anisotropy along that coordinate will be dictated by things far away, and it is then essentially the fact that the sky is dark which states that a ball which falls down is likely to fly apart rather than assemble itself and fly up. This is saying that in the pattern of world-lines there is a general tendency for divergence. This general tendency implies that if we go very far in this coordinate we must find the appropriate boundary condition to produce it. The difficulty, it seems to me, is in understanding how the boundary conditions link in detail each local entropic definition of time. I do not find this process miraculous; I only think it would be nice to understand it in more detail. This does not diminish the problem about our notion of flow of time, however.

BERGMANN

We should be willing, first of all, to make a fundamental distinction between the laws of nature and the boundary conditions.

GOLD

I wonder whether we should give so much status to the distinction between laws and boundary conditions. Essentially we have a single universe. There is only one example of the universe. What use is arbitrariness? It is a remarkable fact that without any effort toward this end, the laws of physics have turned out to possess symmetry and the boundary conditions seem to have turned up in such a way as not to produce symmetry. It seems to me that the world has thus supplied us with a reason for making this distinction. It seems to have arisen naturally in the description of physics. So I think maybe it is basic.

BERGMANN

Yes, but we know that a differential equation with boundary conditions is equivalent to an integral equation. Perhaps the reason for making a distinction between the partial differential equations and the boundary conditions is that in dealing with any natural science, at least to begin with, we pick out the behavior of branch systems which do not interact too strongly with the rest of the universe. This quasi-isolated behavior can be abstracted in solutions of differential equations wherein the interaction of the universe is simplified. As much simplification as possible is made by introducing this interaction in a schematic form by way of boundary conditions.

I agree that the time asymmetry enters physics through cosmology, specifically through the boundary conditions. But describing elementary isolated systems in terms of time-symmetrical coordinates is a matter of our convenience. So it is from convenience that we regard cosmology as introducing the asymmetry. This has to do with Bondi's remark that Lorentz invariance is fine in the small, but utterly ridiculous in the large.

BONDI

This is a purely technical point. Our laws of nature, the differential equations, summarize only certain of the things that we find. Sometimes they include both cases that occur and cases that do not, and in that sense we have a formal restriction in the shape of boundary conditions as perhaps an additional law. But in some cases of course the laws can include these things.

X

But if we had a set of laws which contained among them an asymmetrical law, we would have no problem about the origin of the asymmetry. The problem that we are trying to discuss is this: Can we describe the universe by a set of laws and then discover an experimental asymmetry? (Actually it was discovered that the world was asymmetrical before the law was discovered, but never mind that.) Can we understand this asymmetry in terms of the laws alone? Suppose it is necessary to have another law. What form must this law have? If the analysis had come out differently, there might have been another differential equation having lopsided time, or otherwise this supposition is impossible. It might have been necessary to conclude that the asymmetry was caused not by another asymmetric law but by a different kind of thing, at least different from our present understanding. Perhaps a law might turn up which is asymmetrical in the more conventional sense. It might turn out that although we did not realize it, there existed, as a matter of fact, a time-reversal violator. The whole subject is then changed by that, and it is worthwhile therefore in these provincial times to consider two different kinds of question.

It is a very interesting thing in physics that the laws tell us about permissible universes, whereas we only have one universe to describe. The more laws we get, the more restrictions we have. It could well be that we are missing something, that we have no historical problem in physics, for example, corresponding to evolution in biology. We never ask, "How do the laws get that way?" What are the restrictions that determine what the universe really is, or why the earth is the way it is? The history of the whole universe up to this time has been partially separated, perhaps temporarily, perhaps permanently, from the discussion of physics up to this time. But I do not think it worthwhile to discuss what the laws will look like in the future because the whole aspect of the problem may then have changed.

WHEELER

Suppose our discussion this morning had ended differently, and that we had come out with a complete understanding of time. Then this afternoon we could conclude that it was all nonsense because the discussion about time said nothing about why the universe has all protons, no antiprotons, all electrons, and no positrons. Surely this must have some connection with the one-sidedness of time. The very fact that this has not even come into our discussion shows that we must be fairly far from having come to the real key to the matter.

XI. Observation and the Direction of Time

L. ROSENFELD

I should like to outline a view on this question of the definition of the "earlier-later" relationship, the logical problem at issue here, which Bohr discussed occasionally in conversation. In the literature, the discussion found condensation, as far as I know, only in an article by von Weizsäcker which Grünbaum mentioned earlier. In this article, however, von Weizsäcker has included some considerations of his own with regard to the subjectivity of what he described as the Copenhagen interpretation. These considerations must remain for von Weizsäcker's account, because neither I nor the other people at Copenhagen are prepared to subscribe to this viewpoint.

That there should still be a problem of the direction of time is very paradoxical, in the sense that it is surely a very old problem. We must imagine that people had sense of a flow of time, as Gold emphasizes, long before they knew anything about entropy, cosmology, or the expansion of the universe. In fact, it is interesting to reflect on the way in which the time problem has been introduced in modern science. It is quite striking that in the science of the Greeks, for instance, considerations of time remained on a very rudimentary level, and the absence of workable dynamics in Greek science is typical in that respect. The first scientist who introduced time in dynamical considerations was Galileo, and this was felt as a tremendous progress by his contemporaries, at least by those contemporaries who were able to understand it. There is a famous passage in a letter of Fermat, emphasizing that the great achievement of Galileo, which was destined to revolutionize physics, was just that in his analysis of the motion of falling bodies he tried to find a relationship, not between the height and the velocity of fall, but between the velocity and the time elapsed. That gave the clue to the right solution. But it is also very significant that the way in which

187

Galileo measured the time in his experiments reflected the instinctive elementary feeling of time. He simply used his pulse as a clock, and that of course is an indication that the notion of time was then still on the physiological level, having to do with the feeling of the flow of time that we have from the physiological functions. Even when Newton afterward systematized dynamics, his famous definition of time still referred to a notion of flow. He insisted on the uniformity of flow and it is my guess that his intention was to idealize this physiological feeling, which is of course far from uniform, and to make it workable in physics by idealizing it to be a uniform flow. But then Newton was no further in his analysis than this reference to the feeling of the flow of time. It is one of the most striking features of the physiological processes that they are universal. Physiological processes are always essentially irreversible, so from that point of view there is no problem. If we try to correlate the time that we use in physics with physiological time, then we are adopting a definition implying the irreversibility, and no paradox is felt since all phenomena, including the physical phenomena, even those of motion, are essentially irreversible. Of course the law of inertia, which was also formulated by Galileo and Newton, was thought by them to be an idealization, a limiting law which was introduced only in order to get a simple situation. Surely they thought that actual motions are irreversible, as are all observable motions. Newton was very much concerned about whether the orbits which he had calculated on the basis of the law of inertia were adequate approximations to the actual planetary motions, which he thought were retarded by friction.

GOLD

Newton was aware of the fact that a powerful assumption was involved in his work, insofar as he said, "We must, for these things to be true, believe that there exists an even flow of time." He supposed that there exists an even flow of time, and by saying that he must have been aware that there was an extra assumption involved.

ROSENFELD

But at the same time he unwittingly introduced a paradox, by the fact that the laws of dynamics which he formulated turned out to be reversible in time. That was an unintended accident in his analysis. But this did not worry people much because they still had the notion of causality, implying a succession in time, namely that the effect follows the cause. Yet even that possible basis for keeping an irreversibility of the direction in the physical laws was undermined by Newton himself, who introduced the force of gravity as an instantaneous action at a distance. Surely he was aware of the paradoxical character of this assumption, but he still insisted that it was the correct description of the actual law of gravitation.

Then in subsequent developments, when people began to analyze and formulate the laws of thermodynamics, the idealization of quasi-static phenomena was introduced by Carnot and his followers. This removed from causality the reference to time. Causality now became a relationship between the various magnitudes describing the states of a system, connected by laws expressing reversible transformations, and therefore was completely timeless. At the same time, the observable irreversibility was introduced as a part of the second law, by Clausius. But the problem did not become acute until the statistical approach to the thermodynamic laws was begun by Boltzmann, because previously no one was faced with the comparison between the reversible character of the elementary law and the irreversibility which had to be explained on its basis. Boltzmann, of course, actually introduced a new law in order to produce the irreversibility, namely a statistical element governed by a parabolic equation. It is only when the statistical element is combined with the mechanical laws that we get the irreversibility of the second law.

BERGMANN

The introduction of statistics in this does not by itself produce irreversibility. We must add a specific assumption of asymmetry to the statistics. In the case of Boltzmann's collision law, the assumption is specifically that prior to each collision the incident particles are uncorrelated, whereas the outgoing particles are correlated. Even the introduction of the coarse-grained density distribution is not sufficient to produce irreversible behavior. The trouble with the introduction of the coarse-grained density distribution is that it should take one of the canonical forms, and one should show that the entropy of the ensemble at time t_2 is greater than its entropy at the time t_1. It turns out, since the fact that t_2 is greater than t_1 is used nowhere in the proof, that the entropy actually goes through a minimum at the time t_1, because we make specific assumptions concerning the structure of the ensemble at the time t_1, and the entropy then increases both toward the future and toward the past. That of course is no good, and we must then introduce a specific asymmetric element in addition to coarse-graining. This is a specific assumption that makes a distinction between future and past; coarse-graining alone cannot do that. I am emphasizing this point only because you can see in print time and again that causality plus statistics means irreversibility. I think that is nonsense!

ROSENFELD

I completely agree to this statement; I was thinking of the limiting case in terms of infinite time, but of course it is quite true that the sign of the time is included in the formulation of the problem.

The second law is defined by ascribing a sense of flow to one type of spontaneous irreversible process, such as the conduction of heat. And that implies a sense in time given by the statistical mechanics together with irreversibility and initial conditions.

BERGMANN

We do not go back beyond the initial conditions, to negative times, because we prepare the system so that we can bring in the human operator. The expanding universe is something else.

ROSENFELD

The introduction of statistics is essential, not merely technical help to work out mean values, and describes a situation of observation. The whole problem of the statistical description is conditioned by our scale of observation. If we were Maxwellian demons, of the same size as molecules, we would have no statistical problem; an encounter with a molecule would be of the same magnitude as an encounter with a motor car for us. So the only reason why we bother about introducing temperature and entropy is that we want to have a short cut to the microscopic analysis of the system. This short cut implies curtailing of the information about the system.

BONDI

We contemplate a very large number of initial microstates. Then we smuggle in the notion, "this is a more likely initial state" and "that is a less likely one." It is not the statistical treatment itself that curtails information. The situation is just that we can give vent to our prejudices about the initial conditions.

GOLD

I do not agree that the statistical laws merely show time-asymmetrical behavior, and that this is all there is to be said. When we talk about statistics we are speaking about what we can know. The curtailing of information does not of itself create the novelty of the statistical description.

ROSENFELD

But Boltzmann's equation is a *law*. This parabolic equation which is time-asymmetrical, which contains all of statistical mechanics, all evolution of information, describes the physical state of affairs.

X

We have the equation for the statistical type of law. The physicist merely hopes to explain this law in terms of something else. It is not assumed that this law is really independent of Newtonian laws; it is hoped that this law will be understood in terms of Newtonian law. Such an understanding would produce a paradox, however, because then we would have explained asymmetry on the basis of symmetry.

BERGMANN

It is quite obvious that the Boltzmann equation, far from being a consequence of the laws of classical mechanics, is inconsistent with them.

ROSENFELD

I do not think that the laws of statistics have anything whatever to do with Newtonian laws; they are independent of them. The statistical laws describe the behavior of quantities characterizing large systems of which we have only limited information.

X

The problem is then whether the other apparently symmetrical laws that are already known can serve as a basis for the apparently asymmetrical laws. There is no use assuming that the consequent statistical law is going to be put on the same level as the other; otherwise we have no problem. The problem is the connection between the two points of view, whatever the underlying machinery may be.

MORRISON

The following example may illustrate the problem. If we wish to calculate the evolution of the asteroid belt in a given time, we might use the Boltzmann equation, but it is not likely that we will regard this account to be satisfactory. The asteroid belt is a large system with many degrees of freedom, and yet there is some feeling that the first-order laws must arise by some tampering with the evolution of the dynamical system.

ROSENFELD

Yes. But if we put the initial conditions in a computer, the result would be the trajectories for all time. There would be no irreversible behavior in this respect. We would get fluctuations of a different kind. But if we asked, not about the actual distribution, but about the average density, then we would get a tendency toward time asymmetry for some domains.

LAYZER

Perhaps a different way of formulating this point might help. If we say that irreversible thermodynamics rests on the assumption that knowledge of the present macrostate is enough to predict correctly, but rather roughly, future macrostates, then obviously it is not enough to predict past macrostates, except in the trivial case of equilibrium. This assumption which we do not normally have to formulate really is an assumption that singles out a direction in time.

GOLD

It seems to me that the description in general of the motion of matter always implies apparently time-symmetrical behavior, and that it is only the flow of information, the knowledge about matter, not the matter itself, that introduces the time asymmetry. The moment that we discuss statistical laws, we are in fact concerned not only with the motion of matter but with the information that we can have about it. The reason why the symmetry is different for statistical laws is not because they do not adequately represent the superposition of Newton's laws in the box, but because they are concerned with a new aspect of it, namely, the amount that we can know about the past.

ROSENFELD

It was Bohr's proposal that the essential connection of the observation process with the definition and use of physical concepts, which we have learned from quantum theory, gives us a simple means of defining the direction of time. Time must in this view be directly connected with the observation process. In any observation process there must be a signal coming from the observed system to the recording apparatus, and since the propagation of any signal requires a finite time interval, this gives the possibility of defining the arrival of the signal at the receiver to be "later" than the time of emission. This specification of the sense of time is perfectly general; it applies to all observation processes. In particular, it is not limited to observation of macroscopic systems, as any reference to the usual thermodynamic irreversibility would be.

SCHIFF

How can the emitter and the absorber be distinguished?

ROSENFELD

That is actually decided by the very process of observation. Any observation consists in an interaction between what we choose to call the "object" and what we choose to call the "apparatus." This choice remains the decision of the observer, but once it is taken, then that is decided.

SCHIFF

Then is not the irreversibility really due to the thermodynamical behavior of the observer?

MORRISON

I see that the asymmetry might arise in the internal states of a measurement system; that is a very suggestive idea. I do not see how the asymmetry can arise in the radiative link. In this treatment, we have essentially a radar set, which has the same apparatus as emitter and receiver. The direction in time is not found in the paths of the signals, but in the scattering of the radiation. Apart from this, we cannot distinguish between past and future except by some internal state of the apparatus.

ROSENFELD

This is a point which now has to be looked into. Of course, as is well known, any apparatus of observation must be macroscopic. Therefore, the reception of a signal is a thermodynamic phenomenon associated with a spontaneous process of absorption of radiation. On general grounds, we might expect this in order that our physiological processes may be associated with time as a feature of the world as a whole. We are tempted to say, however, that there is no novelty in this definition of time. As has been emphasized by Bohr in his analysis of observation on the quantum level, it is essential that the part of the system which we consider as apparatus should be treated as a macroscopic body without its functioning being analyzed. The only function of the apparatus is to get a permanent recording of a physical process. Of course, nobody can be forbidden from analyzing this physical function; such an analysis would describe the process as an ordinary absorption of radiation, but this specific process would no longer be the process of "observation." The physical process described must then be given meaning by reference to observation again. The definition of the "earlier-later" relation by reference to the observation process gives this relation a logical status independent of the analysis of the physical process involved.

A similar argument applies to any other concept—for instance, the concept of momentum. We define momentum by means of the principle of conservation of momentum, since the observation process involves the momentum taken up by a macroscopic body. Subsequently we make use of the momentum measured by means of the process in order to check the validity of the principle of momentum conservation. It might be stated that this argument is circular. But this is a situation which exists for all physical concepts. We define length as, say, the property of a rod; we use the property of rigidity of macroscopic bodies in this essential and elementary definition. This kind of circularity is only apparent.

The suggestion then, is to define the "earlier-later" relation in the most elementary way possible by reference to a general feature of every observation process. The advantage which I see in this is the following.

All relevant physical concepts, of course, must be based on physical processes, but it is important to keep the logical definitions and the relationship between concepts clearly separated from the physical statements. This separation can be made if the definitions of concepts are "operational"—that is, related to actual manipulations of apparatus, but involving as little appeal as possible to physical principles. It seems to me that any definition of "earlier-later" should be of that kind, since the appeal to physical regularities involved is very slight indeed. The advantage of this sort of definition is that all statements and all problems connected with irreversibility, or with the sense of time, then become real problems from which all the logical considerations have been separated. If we agree that physical concepts are used in their simple sense, then we know that the questions that we ask have reference to situations in nature and not situations in our minds.

XII. Time and Physical Language[1]

D. L. SCHUMACHER

A discussion about physics ultimately involves language other than that which is usually termed "objective," in which statements may be considered to have the general form, "This quantity has that particular value." This other sort of language has to do with epistemology. Discussions of epistemology, however, often appear to be unproductive. The apparent vagueness of the epistemological question has even tempted many to declare it irrelevant to physics and to rule it out of discussion. This is a counsel of despair; it is possible to discuss in a rigorous way the relationship of physics and epistemology if certain prejudices about physics and its content are scrutinized. A new attitude on this question, quite apart from its general interest, can permit clarification of specific conceptual problems in physics.

A clear example of epistemological interpretation in physics is found in special relativity. The usual view of this theory has of course become centered on the preservation of form in mathematical expressions with respect to a particular group of automorphisms. It is instructive to note, however, that Einstein himself rejected this as a fundamental outlook, in favor of an epistemological view.

The essence of special relativity is that any observer may form physically meaningful communications in terms of that part of description which is proper to any Lorentz frame. In this sense of the word "observer" there is a one-to-one correspondence between observers and Lorentz frames. The restriction upon communication to those quantities and concepts which are not dependent on the choice of observer thus defines what is "physically meaningful." Special relativity is thus a rule of communication. The quantities and concepts which are dependent on the choice of observer are no less "observational" than those which are not, but the linguistic distinction which special relativity makes between them emphasizes particularly that the theory is ultimately making a distinction between the observer and the content of the communications.

This distinction is apparently not part of the content of physical description; it is not "objective" in the usual sense. This remark is in no way intended to single out special relativity as giving rise to such language; it is only a particularly obvious example. Indeed all physical discourse must entail at some level this distinction between the "observer" and the content of the communications, or the "separation between the subject and the object," as it is usually called. This distinction is at the heart of the question of epistemology.

The importance of a careful and judicious application of the principle of distinction or separation between subject and object, and its status as the prime requirement of physical language, have been most strongly emphasized in recent times by Bohr,[2-6] von Neumann,[7] and also implicitly by Schrödinger.[8-10] This principle has been expressed as follows [ref. 7]: "The observation of a physical state can be considered to occur anywhere among the 'object,' 'apparatus,' and 'anatomy' of the observer associated with it, and even into the last arbitrarily deeply." This principle has received recent attention in part because of the details of the present quantum theory of measurement, and this form of the principle uses the terms "object" and "apparatus," which are specifically defined by that theory. These details are not essential to initiate discussion about physical language in general, although we must return to them.

With regard to the general requirements of physical language, the foregoing form of the principle of separation of subject and object may be stated: "The observation, or the separation of subject and object, may be considered to occur anywhere in the world, and even arbitrarily deeply in the brain of the observer" [cf. ref. 5, p. 101].

In spite of the fundamental character of this principle, whatever its explicit form, none of this discussion seems entirely satisfactory, and it is not clear why. On evident grounds of linguistic consistency, the term "separation of subject and object" is itself ambiguous. With respect to the *content* of the description, subject and object should be strictly separate if the description is not to involve apparently nondescriptive words pertaining to "cognition" or "consciousness." But as regards the *origin* of the description, there should rather be a liaison of subject and object if physics is not to proceed vacuously, for if the subject and the object are considered quite apart from each other, then no physical description can be considered to arise at all. The basically analytic idea of physical description suggests that the terms of the principle of separation of subject and object itself should be further examined. This has led to an unproductive analytic regress, particularly in the context of the "mind-body problem."

It should even be expected that the notion of a separation of subject and object is not in this sense self-consistent. This idea is apparently pictorial, and pictures are essentially descriptive. It must not come as too great a surprise that an elementary principle characterizing the language of physical description can not be consistently expressed in a physically descriptive way. This point tends to indicate a different attitude on the question of physical language. The description is the content of the communications; it should evidently not contain reference to the separation between the subject and the content of the communications. A clear distinction is thus indicated between the content of the physical description and the content of statements about the description itself. These two types of content stand in the relationship of language and metalanguage.

If the linguistic supposition of physics in the broadest sense is regarded as a language-metalanguage relationship of these two types of content, with no other requirements, then obvious ambiguities are avoided in the framework of a rule of communication. Any such rule marks the limit of the linguistic analysis, of course, although this limit does not mean that the words "subject" and "object" may not be submitted to judgment concerning their value. Indeed they may be considered to be completely redundant. These words and their equivalents have to a certain extent impeded understanding of the quite fundamental differences between statistical ideas and spatio-temporal or dynamical ideas, for example. A different outlook may prove generally useful.

It is instructive to consider the trends of physiological research, which is fundamentally a part of physical discourse, into the basis of perception. This research has indicated that the function of the brain does not involve a simple one-to-one mapping of the environment onto the cerebral cortex by means of the "sense" organs, which was presumed for so long; the description is far more subtle. As an example, the "sense of sight" must be associated as much with the eye itself and with the connecting nerve tissue as with the cerebral cortex, since *inter alia* there are far more nerve "receptor" cells in the retina than there are information channels in the optic nerve. It may indeed be concluded from this and many other examples that the eye and brain actually "learn to see." Conclusions about perception must be considered with caution, since the limits of descriptive analysis may be reached or overstepped here. An analysis of perception would of course appear inconclusive if the very notion of "perception" is not part of the content of physical description. There are many such examples in physiology which show the linguistic limits of the physical description; the particular terms which imply overstepping the analysis are in quotation marks above. As the outcome of physiological research of this kind, we could expect an expression of the idea of physical language itself, in the form of a dissociation of "perception" in the ordinary sense from the content of the physical description.[11]

The idea that complicated internal states, memory, or signals introduce something linguistically novel into the content of the description is thus suggested in many ways, none of which can avoid the sort of difficulty which is associated with an unanalyzable idea such as "consciousness," which it is the aim of such a suggestion to circumvent. The idea of internal states or memory content has as its implicit purpose the distinction between the content of the description and the successive representation of this content in a set of some type of recording marks. The recording mark is, however, essentially how "memory" and "information" are represented in a visualizable way, and it is the special aim of these concepts to provide a picture in terms of which the records themselves can be used as content of description. It would be misleading to claim some different linguistic status for "representation" and "represented," in this sense. Similarly, a signal is a part of the content of description; as such, the signal itself should not be confused with the content of the signal. The use of the words "memory" and "information" in their present technical sense is therefore to be regarded with a certain wariness [cf. *infra*].

It is one of the fundamental attitudes of cybernetics, stated by Wiener,[12] that a description of the internal states of the brain, or of sufficiently complex computing machines or servomechanisms, can give new insight about logic and language. This view appears to be a novel one, as it is apparently the reverse of the traditional attitude about mechanical function *vis à vis* logic or language. This remarkable view does not however alter the linguistic basis of cybernetics; it devolves in this respect essentially on physical language. The view of cybernetics appears to suggest that the content of physical description can directly influence the rules of language by which that content is expressed, and which comprise its whole meaning. It is very easy in this sort of discussion to overstep the limits of the descriptive analysis. We must return to this particular point.

The statement by Weyl that "the objective world simply *is*, it does not *happen* . . . ," serves as a linguistic model for the discussion about the notions of "time anisotropy" and "time direction." The discussion turns upon a distinction between "things which depend on our consciousness and things which do not." This sort of idea was already clearly criticized in an antinomy by Democritus [quoted in ref. 8]. More specifically, the demonstration of a distinction between the "time anisotropy" and the "time direction" is essentially analytic in character. But this analysis introduces a notion such as "consciousness," which itself implies an overstepping of the analysis. In the context, the idea of "conscious observation" cannot be analyzed further in descriptive terms; a physical description of internal states would push the unanalyzable aspect about, as it were, but the description would not remove it in any case and in particular if the distinction between the "time anisotropy" and the "time direction" is upheld. A distinction of this kind between an "objective" aspect and a "subjective" one cannot be justified by analysis, as it has the status of a "principle" of the language in which the analysis is made.

That this "principle" is not apparently consistent internally and can be formulated or synthesized differently does not, of course, lend strength to an analysis which is typified by Weyl's remark. If indeed the terms "subject" and "object" are considered to be redundant, then use of the terms "subjective" and "objective" to characterize communications or the content of communications is not proper. There are then only consistent communications and inconsistent ones. The unanalyzable notion of an "objective status of events" cannot be employed to "prove" that there is no fundamental difference between statistical ideas and spatio-temporal or dynamical ones.

Indeed we now have simple terms in which to compare the epistemological situation in classical determinist physics with that in statistical physics. In determinist physics the relationship between the content of the physical description (the language) and the content of statements about the description (the metalanguage) seems to be very remote. The idea of a space-time continuum and its inseparable dynamical concepts suggested the possibility of analytic continuation of the total content of the physical description from a part of it given arbitrarily. This was only a suggestion, of course. Any simplification of the dialectical development of physics, necessary for a general term like "classical determinist physics," should not imply specifically that such a description could be complete or closed. Criticism of the classical description can certainly be on a classical level, as is shown by Mach's paradox, for example. But the essential of the classical determinist outlook, which makes this general term meaningful, is the idea that "predictions" and "retrodictions" comprise the whole content of the physical description which proceeds from a (relatively) small amount of arbitrary dynamical data. In view of this powerful aim, it is small wonder that the problem of specifying this arbitrary dynamical data, or what amounts to the separate logical step of cutting the causal analysis, in an almost insignificant part of the "world picture" was considered to be somewhat irrelevant. How very natural it seemed in this outlook to call the content of the description "physics" and the discussion about the description itself "nonphysical." We have yet to escape this attitude even now that we do not accept its premises. If the question of physical language or epistemology retained any interest with respect to the classical determinist description, it was only because the premises of this "world picture" could not be met from the practical point of view.

But what other point of view is there? Statistical physics asks this. In the statistical outlook there is no clear separation between the content of the description and the practical problem of specifying it. The fact that statistical physics forms an epistemic position is well appreciated; a discussion about statistics is basically about what can be stated. It is remarkable in view of the epistemological significance of statistics that this kind of physics should provide an interpretation of an irreversibility which is apparently closely related to the intuitive sense of time.

The statistical irreversibility cannot be deduced from the ascription of a supposed autonomous direction in time to light signals. Time-symmetric electrodynamics together with cosmological boundary conditions makes this ascription. Quite apart from the obvious question of the autonomy of the statistical irreversibility, this view is an example of the prejudgment of issues in physics by the use of picturesque words, and thus places additional emphasis on the need for care in communications. The attempt to establish unambiguously the elementary time sense with electrodynamics depends upon distinguishing two consistent solutions. For this purpose the word "retarded" is associated with one of them and the word "advanced" with the other. But can this linguistic association, which is now the central issue due to the strong prejudgments attached to these words, really be made unambiguously? It has been suggested that in the present case this could be done only by using as a standard the sense in which the universe "expands." However, this conceptual picture is also characterized by two words, "expanding" and "contracting," to which are attached similar prejudgments. How then can the cosmology, which must therefore give the irreversibility of time autonomously, avoid this ambiguity? It is generally held that this can be done *only* by a sort of prejudgment which is essentially probabilistic. This "prejudgment" is a logically independent explicit assumption of irreversibility in addition to and apart from coarse-graining. Cosmology theory has made it possible to regard this assumption as an aspect of statistical boundary conditions, and has thus given the impression that the assumption has to do with the universe as a whole and can therefore be shrugged off as just one of many arbitrary features. However, the characteristic feature of this probabilistic assumption in any application is not that it has some particular descriptive content, but that the assumption itself is a novelty separate from the descriptive analysis. The novelty is in the character of the assumption, not in its explicit content.

In some discussions statistics is defined in a way that attempts to reduce the appearance of novelty, specifically, in such a way that statistics is only coarse-graining or curtailing of information. This is not logically sufficient for a discussion of time, however; probability is excluded. The definition of statistics is of course a matter of convention, but this definition does not alter the fact that the statistical scheme introduces linguistic novelties. Moreover, these novel assumptions of what is likely and what is unlikely themselves produce the statistical irreversibility; without their specific inclusion, there is no irreversibility in the usual sense.[13] Even in the case of external perturbations with coarse-graining, which gives rise to instability, one does not mean "external" merely in the sense of "external to the system in question," but rather "external to the *analysis* of the system"; a statistical fluctuation or perturbation is the point at which the analysis is cut off. It would be only misleading to regard the idea of time which has been given by statistical theory as an entirely descriptive "anisotropy," for this tends to suppress the novel aspects.

Indeed it may be expected from the unanalyzable character of the distinction between the "time anisotropy" and the "time direction" that the notions which give rise to characteristic features of statistical physics should be of a linguistically novel kind, or distinct from the content of descriptive language.

The basis of the concepts introduced by statistical physics can be examined to a certain extent, however, in terms of the idea of physical language which was suggested above. This makes the novelty of the statistical language apparent. In this conception it is fairly evident that the term "probability," involved in the assumption of irreversibility, is not part of the content of description. It seems more reasonable to regard it as a part of the metalanguage. In this respect, a close analogy could be drawn between the probability and a related notion in the metalanguage, the truth value ("true" or "false"). The idea of probability is remarkable in this way since it is usually viewed as a construct of statistical theories. This usual view does not mean, however, that the linguistic basis of "probability" or statistics in the general sense must be the same as that of the constructs of other kinds of physical theories, namely dynamical and spatio-temporal concepts.

The ideas of probability and truth value are intimately connected with the so-called "intuitive" sense of time. This connection can be shown by expressing these notions in terms of each other. It may be generally acceptable to express the idea of "intuitive progress of time" as follows, for example: "It is in the 'future' that descriptions (either predictions or retrodictions) which are only 'probable' are assigned a definite 'truth value.'" *The idea of the progress of time is an outgrowth of the linguistic forms for physical communications*, not so much of the content of physical description, and is thus a part of the epistemological question. This view amounts, of course, to a sharp break between the "intuitive" time and the notion of time which is owed to Newton and to Minkowski, for example. This may be taken as a criticism of the very notion of time as a coordinate. Since the notions of probability and truth value are linguistically similar, and since they are apparently equivalent for numerical probabilities unity and zero, it is perhaps not too meaningful to retain a verbal distinction between them. On the other hand, numerical probabilities for descriptions are assigned in general only on the basis that some description is assigned a probability of unity.

This approach may help to clarify the well-known question of the two separate aspects of probability. These two aspects are often called the "random," or "inductive," aspect and the "*a priori*," or "deductive," one, and it has not been possible to reconcile these with each other. This question, as well as the failure of attempts to show that there is no novelty in statistics, that is, to show that statistics can be analyzed in terms of, or derived from, the language of determinist physics, will perhaps appear strikingly similar to the outcome of the program to make an analysis or justification of logical induction. It was recognized only after the greatest exertions that the very notions of "analysis" and "justification" themselves imply *deduction*, and that the idea of "induction" is linguistically distinct, not to be comprehended in such a treatment. This is perhaps not only an analogy; *it may be practically the same thing, for the inductive or synthetical feature of physical description may be regarded to constitute terms of understanding for the "random" aspect of probability.* Thus it is the aspect of randomness which contains the novelty. This also applies to the analogous ideas of information and noise, which are by no means absolutes if they are correctly interpreted. Of course the term "*a priori*," as well as "*a posteriori*," "objective," and "subjective," which appear in connection with probability, must not be taken too seriously, as they tend to obscure the issue. The inductive character of randomness makes clear the reason for the difficulty of associating a measure with randomness. The concept of a measure is an analytic one; an attempt to associate a measure with randomness gives rise to (formal or informal) statements containing internal contradictions essentially equivalent to the phrase "order of disorder."

Insofar as it has been possible to make a reasonable characterization of physical language with a finite number of words, the idea of language and metalanguage can help to reduce the dependence of our discussions upon some words or statements which are unanalyzable or which contain prejudgments. This is all that can be claimed for any rule or principle, however; they are only makeshifts for simplifying and limiting the discussion. It should not come as a great surprise, although it usually does, when principles lose their usefulness. This attitude should extend even to the content of the principles or characterizations of the language itself, no matter how general or natural they may appear to be. The need for such an attitude may also be regarded as a feature of the synthetical aspect of language in general. In this respect, there are of course many theories which in addition to making specific statements in physical description, also change in many ways the terms or lexicon of the description itself, so it is not reasonable to separate physical description in general from the content of the theoretical structure or logical algorisms, which are an extention of ordinary communication.

Whereas the distinction between the language and the metalanguage is quite pronounced as regards the content of "classical determinist" theories, this distinction is not so clear in "statistical" or "probabilistic" theories. However, nobody denies, of course, that the language of statistical theories is a part of physics. That this might depend upon not analyzing the language of certain theories too deeply in terms of principles is not relevant; what we call "physics" is conventional no matter how deeply or accurately this notion can be expressed. This outlook indicates that the very linguistic basis of physics in general has been fundamentally altered by the statistical theories. This has been guessed by some authors, notably Schrödinger [ref. 10]. The attitude of determinist theories suggests that the whole terms of discussion, including the content of physical description as well as its metalanguage, would be called "epistemology," distinct from the content of the description alone. In the spirit of the "novel" theories which have modified this outlook, the language and the metalanguage both would likely be termed "physical language." The idea of time has been the most obvious criticism of the "world picture" by the statistical outlook, but time is not really favored for criticism, contrary to appearances.

The dominent role of careful and consistent communication in physics has been recognized in recent times primarily by Bohr, whose writing is itself a paragon of precise and intellectually scrupulous communication. It is this attitude toward physical language which enabled Bohr's simple and effective replies to many criticisms of the quantum mechanical scheme which were proposed. These criticisms were in essence ambiguities or inconsistencies of language. Bohr has stressed in particular that the criticism of the classical dynamical concepts which is implied in the uncertainty relations is itself ambiguous. An unambiguous criticism of the classical dynamical concepts which was urged by Bohr has become known as the principle of complementarity [*vide* ref. 6].

The principle of complementarity can be stated or interpreted in various ways, so long as it is done carefully. It is an essential point that the word "quantum" characterizes a particular type of physical description; it does not refer in a primary way to the content of the description or to part of the content. The aim of the complementarity principle is a definition of "quantum description," which does not mean "description of quanta." The principle may be stated: "To mutually exclusive experimental conditions there correspond distinct experimental outcomes which taken together in a complementary way form a complete quantum description." Complementarity, contrary to what seems to be the customary view in theoretical physics, is just as fundamental as formal quantum mechanics, which is its algorism. If the formalism were eventually brought into conflict with the principle of complementarity somehow, then it would be quite wrong to call that formalism a "quantum" formalism, whether or not it were shown on other empirical grounds to be correct.

The statement of the principle of complementarity suggests that the term "experimental conditions" should be further analyzed. This idea involves the terms "object" and "apparatus," whose joint specification is equivalent to a choice of a particular experimental condition. The principle of complementarity therefore requires that the distinction between the "object" and the "apparatus" must be a moveable one, if a complete description is to be encompassed by the principle. This conclusion, which is compelled by a need for consistent communication of experimental results, could not have failed to strike Bohr with its suggestive similarity to the "principle of separation of subject and object." This is particularly shown by Bohr's interchangeable use of the terms "subject and object" and "apparatus and object" in the quantum mechanical formalism.

This point has caused confusion, particularly with regard to von Neumann's treatment of the quantum theory of measurement and its subsequents. A certain dispute between Bohr and von Neumann is seen to hinge upon von Neumann's arbitrary fixed *labeling* "object," "apparatus," (and "observer"), as parts of the formalism, and the further proof that the "observation" can be considered to "take place" anywhere among them [cf. ref. 7, Ch. VI]. Von Neumann's view is that the "principle" of physical language, namely, the "principle of separation of subject and object," should not be violated by any formal theory of measurement, and that such a violation would result if it were shown that the "observation" must "occur" at a particular point.

In view of this attitude, which seems *prima facie* reasonable, it appears that the use of the terms "subject and object" for "apparatus and object" is not reasonable. However, this terminology may be regarded to have a special purpose. The effect of these terms is that the specification of the experimental conditions, or the labeling of "object" and "apparatus," must not be analyzed further. The principle of complementarity stresses that the very labeling of "object" and "apparatus" must not be fixed; this defines the quantum description, so the statement of the complementarity principle is not itself descriptive.

The dispute between Bohr and von Neumann about the epistemological basis of the quantum theory of measurement might be imagined to run as follows:

N: "A clear distinction between the object and the apparatus is essential to me, and I can distinguish between them in a way which is internally consistent and purely descriptive. The 'object' is that part of the world which is considered to exhibit quantum effects, and the 'apparatus' is the part which is not."

B: "The clear distinction between the 'object' and the 'apparatus,' the specification of the experimental conditions, is no less important to me, but the very word 'quantum,' or 'quantum effects,' can refer only to the *whole* description, including *both* the experimental outcome *and* the specification of the experimental conditions."

N: "All right, I can call the 'object' that part of the world which is affected by the mutual object-apparatus interaction, and the 'apparatus,' the part which is not affected by it."

B: "What do you mean, 'affected by interaction'? The apparatus is affected in the sense that there is an irreversible registration of a recording mark in it. From the trend of your arguments it is clear that you wish to regard that as part of the content of physical description."

N: "So I do, but the 'object' and the 'apparatus' can still be consistently distinguished analytically. The 'object' is *dynamically* affected by the interaction of the two, and the 'apparatus' is not *dynamically* affected by it."

B: "In using or implying a phrase like 'dynamical influence of the apparatus on the object,' you are ultimately denying the principal point that quantum theory demonstrates, that the content of the quantum mechanical description is not separable from the specification of the experimental conditions."

It seems very difficult to stop the analysis at this point. This imaginary discussion might proceed as follows:

N: "But are not *both* the 'object' and the 'apparatus' *parts of our world* in the most general sense? If so, we certainly ought to be able to include them both in the content of an internally consistent description."

B: "But we were talking about *quantum* description. You are now talking about some other type of description, to which the term 'quantum' cannot be applied. You have made the common mistake of using the term 'world' as if it had some meaning which is entirely independent of the content of the physical description. These terms 'object' and 'apparatus' do not denote 'parts of the world,' one part obeying one sort of law and the other, another. The principle of complementarity takes the place of the 'principle' of physical language whose preservation is a feature of your formal treatment of measurement. As such a principle, complementarity is not itself part of the physical description."

The language of quantum theory, as set forth by Bohr, requires implicitly a separation between the *content* of the quantum description and the *content* of the rule by which it is expressed or characterized. The principle of complementarity thus not only takes the place of concepts like the "principle of separation of subject and object," but it criticizes them for their appearance of being descriptive. Bohr is sometimes reproached for his application of the complementarity idea to far wider issues and circumstances than the evidence which led to this principle seems to involve. However, insofar as complementarity is an expression of the idea of physical language itself, its applicability is of course most general [cf. refs. 2–5].

The specific content of the complementarity principle was of course arrived at without referring to the ideas of statistics explicitly or offering any new fundamental interpretation of those ideas. Complementarity therefore, as to be expected, emphasizes the distinction between quantum theory and all other theories, rather than the distinction between statistical theory in general and other theories. The question about which of these differences is deeper arises quite often and in a variety of ways. One way of posing this question indirectly is by asking the following: If the experimental situation in quantum theory is fixed arbitrarily, then how should one speak of the predictions and retrodictions, which are apparently of an essentially statistical character? Are the recording marks to be considered as "objective," or as "subjective"? Are they "observed," or not? These questions are frequently asked in connection with complementarity and with the formal theory of measurement,[14] but in the precise terms of reference already specified, a direct answer to this sort of question would press the descriptive analysis too far, as this would ultimately entail an equivocation of a fundamental kind.

Further, the question might be asked whether the irreversibility in quantum theory is of a statistical character or is defined, as Bohr suggested, only by the sense of transmission of a signal from the "object" to the "apparatus." The latter definition cannot be submitted to criticism by further analysis without in effect analyzing the distinction between the "object" and the "apparatus," which would be equivalent to questioning the principle of complementarity itself. The formal theory of measurement, on the other hand, suggests that the irreversibility is an essentially statistical one and that the irreversibility is not fundamentally different from the one given by statistical theory to which the term "quantum" cannot be applied. The formal theory of measurement has tended to emphasize the distinction between statistical theory in general and other theories, rather than a distinction between "quantum" and "non-quantum" statistical theories. It might however be argued that if the term "quantum" is defined only as the mode of description which is characterized by the principle of complementarity, then the questions regarding the statistical character of the predictions and retrodictions are logically quite external to quantum theory, as so defined. In this respect, quantum theory may be regarded as a novel criticism of the language of determinist description.

Of course, such a view as this would now also be considered extreme. The usual view now surely is that complementarity includes statistical notions in some implicit way, and that it has its particular content only because of the essentially statistical character of the predictions and retrodictions. This view is, however, not explicitly justifiable and should not be taken to suggest that quantum theory could be reducible to any theory to which the term "quantum" cannot be applied. The interpretation of the predictions and retrodictions as probabilistic may be regarded as a separate step which does not pertain especially to the term "quantum." The independent assumption of "distinct and individual quantum [*sic*] processes" under specified experimental conditions renders the predictions and retrodictions inherently statistical. But this meaning of the term "quantum" is entirely different from the previous meaning, and *these meanings cannot be deduced from each other*.

If complementarity and statistics are logically distinct, then why does the relationship between them seem to be so intimate? The questions regarding the logical status of the predictions and retrodictions in quantum theory are based on difficulties in application of the idea of physical language which have been outlined. It can be reasonably clear that the notion of physics itself as well as the content of physical theories evolves in a synthetical or dialectical way, but this is not clear unless an attempt is made to state the notion of physical language in a satisfactory way. The formulation of the principle of complementarity may be regarded as an attempt to do this kind of synthesis. It is indeed evident from his writings that Bohr did regard the principle of complementarity as an essential clarification of the idea of physical language. The novelties of statistics and complementarity are somewhat similar in intention. Anything more than this cannot necessarily be said; if each were expressible in terms of the other, then they would be justifiable in terms of each other, or reducible to each other.

While Schrödinger perhaps did not fully recognize the linguistic basis of the "world view," he was most of all aware of its peculiar and historically contingent aspects [cf. refs. 8–10].

The remarks above are of course translatable into terms concerning the formal algorism of quantum mechanics. The equations involving the elements and subsets of the Hilbert space are essentially sets of statements in the metalanguage; they constitute sets of statements about statements in the language of dynamics. The "quantum" rules for expressing relationships concerning the Hilbert space then may be interpreted to constitute rules of composition in a propositional calculus relating statements expressed in the language of dynamics. These rules themselves are not logically a part of dynamics. The "quantum state vectors" thus do not refer to a peculiar type of object, but to statements. The paper, "The Logic of Quantum Mechanics," by Birkhoff and von Neumann [*Ann. Math.* **37** (1936), 823], proposing of formal equivalence of the noncommutative algebra on the elements and subsets in Hilbert space with a lattice of statements which does not satisfy the distributive rule of composition is of course quite consonant with the present remarks. The epistemological assumptions in the paper of Birkhoff and von Neumann are not entirely clear and unambiguous, possibly for heuristic intentions. These present remarks, however, may to a certain extent reduce the motivation for assertion of the formal equivalence proposed in that paper.

It seems difficult to accept that there should not be some final logical or linguistic completeness notwithstanding, for example, the failure of programs in logic such as Hilbert's, and it is usually thought that in any case there are limitations on the human brain which could provide such a completeness. The hope for limitations amounts only to the view that the content of physical description could somehow delimit physical language itself. This aspect of description brings up questions of genetics and biological evolution which should be discussed further in this context. The usual view of the human being in biological evolution is that a nervous system which has evolved to a definite high degree of complexity implies a decisive intervention into the environment of the organism, so as to preserve the form of the organism. This appears to present "natural" limitations upon an important part of the content of physical description.

In the first place, the behavioral intervention into environment can be decisive for the emergence of characteristics, regardless of the complexity of the nervous system or the form of the characteristics. In a very general way, relatively small specializations tend to be amplified by the interaction of the organism and the environment: the specialization affects the behavior which further favors the specialization. The behavior, environment, and form of the organism, including the genetic structure, are so closely interrelated that it is hardly possible to make any distinction between them as content of physical description. Indeed, such distinctions have probably been the source of difficulties with the ideas of Darwinism.

In the case of man, this interrelation of the behavior, environment, and structural form is in principle the same; it is only more complex. For example, the content of the description of human behavior includes all the signals which humans make (not to be confused with the *content* of the signals), and which further influence the behavior. This complexity is only a matter of degree, so it should not be taken to define the word "human." The most direct interrelation of this kind is through the genetic coding. Even production of an organism in arbitrarily close accordance with a preliminary genetic specification does not involve any essential novelties; this would be only a more direct interrelation. If the interrelation of behavior, environment, and structure is not in general so direct as an intervention in the content of the DNA which carries genetic information (but not all relevant information), then the interrelation is only a more diverse process; it is no less important. In view of the generality of this interrelation, it does not seem reasonable to claim that structural form and behavior which is loosely and prejudicially termed "human" impose any limitations on biological development.

Biological "evolution" was in fact an implicitly novel or epistemological scientific theory, and it was also a theory of "irreversibility." Biological evolution and statistical physics share the same epistemological language.[15] This language implies internally a cutting of the descriptive analysis. It seemed, of course, unreasonable that there should be a causal descriptive analysis of behavior, environment, and anatomic structure, although the barrier to this analysis is not to be found in descriptive terms; this means that the epistemological motivations for Darwinism are quite the same as those for statistical physics. So terms like "evolution" and "adaptation," *no less than a term like* "*volition*," permit cutting the analysis. This is logically or linguistically the same as stipulating that random fluctuations in the genetic material produce structural variety for selection.

Any communication, including the content of these pages, depends as much upon not defining or analyzing certain words or statements as upon analyzing others. The terms of physical communications can be analyzed in the framework of the principle of physical language, or the principle of separation of subject and object. However, if this seemingly descriptive principle is analyzed itself in the general context of descriptive language, it is seen to be equivocal. It is nevertheless possible to state a nondescriptive characterization of physical language which allows analysis of physical communications and which evidently does not demand further analysis in descriptive language. To start with, this removes the need for words such as "subject" and "object," whose analysis is difficult to avoid. But, by consequence, the unambiguous characterization of physical language shows the linguistic basis of the ideas of probability and epistemology which subsume the notion of the progress of time. In particular, the elementary idea of progress of time which is in the synthetical aspect of language can be connected to the statistical irreversibility *via* the idea of randomness. On the one hand, the characterization of physical language defines the limits of the analytic description, but on the other, the discussion as a whole may be interpreted to mean that this characterization is an historically contingent one which is synthetical but not of necessity logically prior to other statements. How this is viewed depends on what is analyzed and what is not.

The writer wishes to thank G. Miller and P. Szekeres for many helpful discussions.

XIII. Nuclear Moments and Time Symmetry

L. SCHIFF

If there are such things as nuclear moments of a non-time-reversal-invariant type, then they might be used to establish the direction of time.

Let us begin with a classical picture. Figure XIII-1(a) shows a wire

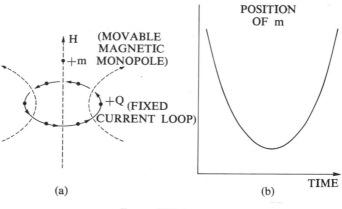

FIGURE XIII-1

which is carrying current consisting of positive charges. The current produces a magnetic field which in conventional terminology appears as indicated. We must not think about the fields except as constructs. We should consider only what we can see and photograph with a motion-picture camera. We can photograph charges $+Q$ going around in the direction of the arrow. We can also imagine that a positive magnetic monopole, which is odd with respect to time reversal, is thrown in along a field line. It will be opposed by the field and so will go in some distance, then turn around and come back. We can photograph this whole situation, if it exists, in which a positive charge goes around the

214

loop and a monopole goes in and out again, as in Figure XIII-1(b). When we run the film backwards, the positive charge reverses its direction of motion, as does the magnetic monopole, since the motion was symmetric. The laws of physics say, however, that this is an impossible motion because the motion of the electric charge is reversed, the magnetic field is reversed, and therefore a monopole thrown in the same way would go on through and accelerate out.

X

But suppose the monopole has helicity. Then this monopole may be only one of two kinds. Suppose that there is a hook hanging out of a monopole, by which we can tell its sign. Perhaps this hook is time-dependent, like a wheel that spins in the opposite direction in the reversed motion picture. If there are two such different monopoles, the situation may be time reversible.

BONDI

In the case of the charges, we know which way they are going around because positive charges look different from negative charges on the film. If positive monopoles look the same as negative monopoles, then the chap who looks at the backward-running thing and who has no independent knowledge of whether it is a positive or negative monopole, can only tell its sign from its motion. He will therefore say, arbitrarily, "This is a negative monopole." Only if all positive monopoles in the world were red, and all negative monopoles were green, would the picture give enough information to establish a direction of time.

SCHIFF

I am assuming that there is only one kind of monopole, and one kind of charge. If we make only the time reversal, then a physically disallowed situation arises. That is all. This remark is meant to give a classical picture of what happens if we assume that such things exist in this particular way.

MORRISON

What if only electric monopoles exist, and no magnetic monopoles?

SCHIFF

The interaction of two charges with one another is completely reversible from the well-known laws of electrodynamics and Newton's laws. It is usually said that Newton's laws and Maxwell's equations are time-reversible. These are time-reversible if there are charges but no monopoles, or if there are monopoles but no charges, but not if there are both.

I am trying to describe classically what we normally say in terms of quantum-mechanical matrix elements for non-time-reversal-invariant interactions.

Now let us consider the magnetic dipole, as in Figure XIII-2(a). The cylinder now represents the magnetic dipole. I want to describe what is well known: that as regards time symmetry, we do not get into any

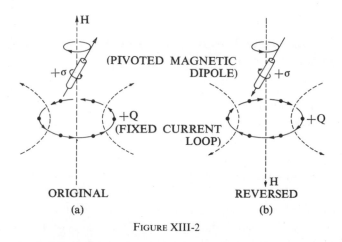

FIGURE XIII-2

trouble with a magnetic dipole. The magnetic dipole consists of some sort of a rotating object, which has angular momentum as well as magnetic moment. We are ultimately interested in nuclear magnetic dipoles. The little loop shows the direction of rotation, so the angular momentum is along the direction of the arrow. Since the magnetic dipole moment is parallel to the angular momentum, the precession is in the direction of the larger loop. Remember that the field in which the object is precessing is also produced by a ring of charges $+Q$. If a film of this process is run backwards, as in Figure XIII-2(b), the charge appears to reverse, the field reverses, the angular momentum reverses, and the precession reverses. So we get an allowed motion, because by reversing everything we still get a situation which is realized in nature.

Now let us consider a third example which is the most interesting

from the experimental point of view. This is the case of an electric dipole moment in an electric field, Figure XIII-3(a). We have an electric field produced by a charge $+Q$ with electric field lines radiating from it. We also have a rotating object which is assumed to have an electric dipole moment parallel to its angular momentum. This object might,

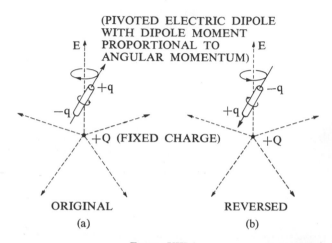

FIGURE XIII-3

for example, be a neutron, which has an inherent magnetic dipole moment, or a nucleus of He³. We can see that if a film of its motion is run backwards, the E field is invariant; the angular momentum is reversed, so that the electric dipole moment is also reversed. The dipole now precesses in the wrong direction. This may be looked upon as a mixed monopole-charge situation, if we consider the electric dipole moment to be made up of a magnetic monopole moving in a circle. So an electric dipole or a magnetic monopole would not permit time-reversal invariance, and might be used to establish a direction in time.

MORRISON

No. If we interchange the definitions "electric" and "magnetic" throughout, we can always make the descriptions symmetrical in time.

SCHIFF

Maybe the problem is in the words. If we photograph a physically possible situation, reverse the photograph, and get a physically impossible situation, then we can perhaps establish a direction of time.

GOLD

No. There is no way of recognizing which kind of monopole we have, except by observing the orbit it makes. Then we have no way of specifying an arrow of time, although what you claim is perfectly right.

X

Are you claiming that if another particle were discovered, the "schiffon," which happens to have an angular momentum and an electric dipole moment, then you could define the direction of time? There could be two kinds of schiffons, equally easy to produce, that have a symmetry, the "pro" and the "contra." That is, there are those which have their electric dipole in the direction of the angular momentum and those which have the opposite orientation. And there must be just that symmetry if we are able to produce these particles in equal numbers from the same particles in the same way. With both in the world we cannot tell which photograph is which.

SCHIFF

We can use heavy nuclei, which might be expected to have a definite kind of electric dipole moment. A film of their motions run backwards will not represent motions of real nuclei. I am talking about the real world in which there are not equal numbers of particles and anti-particles.

Now, as is well known, we can divide all moments into two classes. The "even" ones are the electric monopole or charge, the magnetic dipole moment, and so on; the "odd" ones are the magnetic monopole, the electric dipole moment, and so on. A search has been made for the magnetic monopole; nothing has been found having a certain production cross section which is extremely small. How about looking at the higher moments, the dipole, quadrupole, and so on, for existing particles? It turns out that the simplest case to look for is the electric dipole moment. If the object is not a neutron but a hydrogen chloride molecule which has a permanent electric dipole moment, what then? Suppose first that it does not have any angular momentum, but that the moment is related to the figure axis. Then when the moment is pulled out of line with the electric field and released, it will tend to swing over into line again. If we now reverse the motion, of course it still swings over. There is no conflict with time invariance in the case of known molecular electric dipole moments. The conflict occurs only when the electric

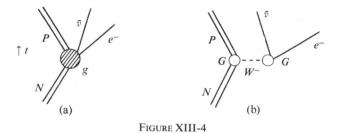

FIGURE XIII-4

dipole moment is inseparably tied to the angular momentum of the particle.

First we should ask where these electric dipole moments might come from, since there is pretty good evidence that the electric moments are small. In the case of the neutron, an upper limit has been set which is very small. We look for these things not in the strong interactions, but in the weak interactions. We can describe in Figures XIII-4 and XIII-5 the way in which these appear. Figure XIII-4(a) represents neutron decay by the ordinary beta decay process in which the neutron disintegrates into a proton, an antineutrino, and a negative electron with an interaction which is represented by the coupling constant g. Another likely possibility for treating this decay process is that the neutron does not decay directly into all three of these things, but decays first into a proton and a particle which is called an intermediate charged vector boson W, as in Figure XIII-4(b). This particle is supposed to carry the weak interaction from the neutron-proton system to the electron-neutrino system, where it disintegrates to produce the electron and

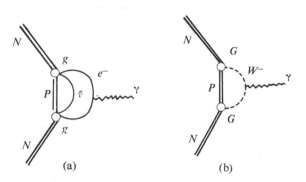

FIGURE XIII-5

antineutrino. The point of Figure XIII-4 is to show that in (a) a single interaction is involved; in (b) two interactions are involved. For a given decay rate, we have $g \sim G^2$.

Now we consider what happens if the neutron, or any other neutral particle, is to have an electric dipole moment. There must be an interaction of some sort with the electromagnetic field which is represented schematically as a photon line. So only a weak interaction can introduce the possible lack of time-reversal invariance. In the first scheme, Figure XIII-5(a) the neutron decays into a proton and gives off a neutrino and electron, which then are recaptured to reconstitute the neutron. But while the neutron is broken up, a photon interacts with the electron. It is this interaction with the two non-time-reversal-invariant vertices which produces the electric dipole moment. The same process can occur with the W particle without the interposition of the electron and neutrino, as in Figure XIII-5(b). The point of this is that if the interaction involves the intermediate boson, a factor G^2 enters. If it were a Fermi interaction, there would be a factor g^2. Therefore, the boson interaction will be much stronger than the Fermi interaction because only one power of $g \sim G^2$ comes in the former, while two powers of g enter the latter, and g is a small number. So if we can do the measurement, this is of interest as a point of elementary-particle physics because it might decide between the two interactions. The detailed calculations have not been done, so I cannot quote any numbers. We must assume lack of time symmetry of the matrix elements. Also, they are both quite divergent, so there are cutoff problems.

The way in which Fairbank and Hamilton at Stanford plan to do the experiment with the electric dipole is very simple in principle. We place a He^3 nucleus in an electric field and measure the precession rate. Of course, when the nucleus is put in an electric field it accelerates, so the experiment is somewhat difficult. We are dealing with moments which are so small that it is difficult to keep the nucleus in the field long enough to get a reasonable change of angle. So the problem is how one can get an electric field at a nucleus.

The argument that I have just given is the classical one, but it can be translated into quantum mechanics. It turns out that if there is any combination of charged particles with electrical interactions, then there is never any first-order interaction between the charged particles and an external field. This can be shown generally. This treatment assumes that all the forces involved are electrostatic; in fact they are not, because we know that nuclei have magnetic moments, and also have nonelectrical forces in them. One way of seeing the effect of the latter is to notice that a nucleus has a finite size. If we know that it has a finite size, we can realize that the electric-field interactions, which would be zero if the nucleus were a point, are no longer necessarily zero. Consider the specific case of He^3 with two electrons around it. If this were a point nucleus in an external field, the electron cloud around the nucleus would distort itself so as to cancel out the external field at the nucleus. But since it has a finite size, there is actually at the nucleus a small average field whose order of magnitude is the external field multiplied by the square of the ratio of the nuclear radius to the atomic radius. Unfortunately, this latter is a factor of order 10^{-9}, so the experiment is difficult; otherwise it would be easy. Inclusion of the nuclear magnetic moment increases this reduction factor to about 10^{-7}. So the problem is: Can we measure precession in fields of this order when the external field has a reasonable value?

X

With a neutron in the field, a situation which is much harder to maintain technically, we do not have this problem. We can put the electric field on directly, so we have the factor 10^7 in our advantage. Does the ease of handling the helium compensate that 10^7?

SCHIFF

Yes, it can. The technique consists in getting rid of the magnetic field completely. The Purcell-Smith-Ramsay experiment, which set the limit on the electric dipole of the neutron, was done by measuring precessing neutrons in a beam going through a magnetic field, then superimposing an electric field and measuring the change in precession frequency. We cannot do this with the He^3 nucleus because even a very small magnetic field will cause a large precession, so that we cannot measure a small electric moment. To do the experiment, we must get *zero* magnetic field by using flux quantization—expel the field completely. If we have less than one fluxoid, and reduce it to zero, then we know that the field is exactly zero. Then we start with polarized He^3 nuclei and measure the change in flux linkage through a loop. In this way we can measure a precession angle of about a second or so of arc. The angle is measured by induced current in a superconducting loop which encloses the polarized He³ nucleus. We are not measuring the frequency of precession; we are measuring a very small fraction of one precession period. By this means, we hope to get sensitivities better than those in the neutron experiment.

BERGMANN

The asymmetry of nature with respect to parity transformations is resolved in a higher symmetry by taking a charge conjugation along with the parity transformation. Am I right in believing that if we were to discover this oddness with respect to time reversal, then we could resolve this asymmetry by introducing or discovering a new type of supercharge conjugation C' which is not identical with the usual charge conjugation?

SCHIFF

First, if we believe the TCP theorem, then a breakdown of T invariance imples a breakdown of CP invariance. That is all we can say. If we do not believe TCP theorem, then it might be possible to maintain CP invariance and yet break down T invariance.

BERGMANN

Perhaps there exist not only two particles which are in a sense mirror images, what we now call particles and antiparticles, but four particles. So there should be a second kind of transformation which therefore requires four different particles, the neutron, the neutron prime, and antineutron and antineutron prime, where "prime" indicates that the electric dipole moment is reversed. C' is definitely not the same transformation as C, since it would not reverse the sign of the electric charge.

X

I think there is some evidence that such particles as these "primes" do not exist. If there were another neutron-like object which differed only in the size of its moment, then it could get into the same state as the other neutrons. Since the exclusion principle limits the character of nuclei, there would be new kinds of nuclei and new kinds of states that we have not seen before. They would presumably be produced in pairs when antiprotons are made. Anyway, these would constitute a little bit of background dirt, peculiar substances which could be collected chemically.

General Discussion

MORRISON

What connection between an air raid shelter and the rest of the universe is required in order to produce a significant marking of the time direction? In my view, only a minimal connection, one which could be described in an almost time-independent way, is needed to establish a unique direction of time in almost closed systems.

Besides the three types of time markers we have seen, the nonstatic metric, the wiggling charges, and the box of gas, let me produce a fourth one. This is a gram of radium without helium, in a bank vault, together with a device for measuring its size, such as a micrometer. In order to have this arrangement, there must be the sort of universe which allows the construction of a gram of radium and the evacuation of helium from a sizable region of space. That is all which is required from the cosmology. I am not sure that this is a different case; I just raise this, which may lead to other questions.

HOYLE

I think this question of decoupling is vital. I am not sure that we can really decouple the box from the rest of space, as you maintained. There is a sort of counterexample. There are π machines which are obviously not decoupled, but which actually make entropy go the other way; these are ourselves. In evolution, the mutations of the π machine come into operation and produce the random fluctuations. Then the message gets better as time goes on.

MORRISON

The mutations are very wasteful; the total message does not get better. It is only that there is a piece of the message which does.

223

ROSENFELD

It appears that the observer, or the decision to make an observation of a system, introduces the time asymmetry for the system. While listening to the expressions of opinion in the course of these three very stimulating days, I have noticed that there emerged a consensus in that direction. In the case of thermodynamics, for instance, Bondi emphasized that a sense of time is not implied in the definition of the thermodynamical quantities, nor in laws relating those quantities insofar as those laws are expressed by equations, but is introduced as soon as we make this cut between ourselves and the isolated systems left to themselves. In the case of radiation, I think that the situation is the same. A decision to use retarded potentials is entirely conditioned by the situation of observation. We either decide or are obliged to accept initial conditions. The Wheeler-Feynman analysis, in its early days, was just to show that apparent one-sidedness in time, introduced by the choice of retarded potentials, does not really conflict with the symmetry of the equations. Rather, this choice corresponds to a physical situation in which we know at a certain time what the sources of radiation are, and do not bother about the future fate of the radiation. This is symbolized in the Wheeler-Feynman theory by the existence of the large absorbing object.

I would like to see the question of time formulated differently as regards cosmology. Perhaps we ought not to speak of a cosmological arrow of time at all. Perhaps we ought to formulate physics as local problems with the device of a time variable. The sense of time then can be defined through our observation of any part of the universe and in terms of the physical description which uses this time variable. If we have evidence of an expansion of the universe, where the word "expansion" is uniquely defined by our convention, then we can ask the following question to which a definite meaning is attached: Is it possible that the same laws and the same course of events described by statistical considerations are compatible with a contracting phase? Or, to what extent would the contracting phase arise?

BERGMANN

In my view, if it is assumed that the second law of thermodynamics holds and in a form to be consistent with our customary arrow of time (which in turn is intimately related to the way we operate both as physical systems and as sentient beings), then a hot star must radiate rather than act as a sink of radiation. A star could not be a sink of radiation if it is hot. The concept of temperature is time-symmetric, so there is no one-sidedness smuggled in by this concept. If the universe is relatively free of photons, then obviously it is in the direction marked as "future" by the second law that the stars radiate into the vacuum. The stars radiate until the vacuum is filled with black-body radiation at the same temperature as the stars themselves. As long as the stars are hotter than the surrounding photon-filled vacuum, we must have radiation going out from the stars. If we make the "weak cosmological assumption" that the universe is isotropic and homogeneous, then not only do we get into the difficulties of Olbers' paradox, but we get into much worse difficulties. We get divergence. The light is infinitely bright. This is certainly as unacceptable a situation as was, say, the ultraviolet catastrophe of classical equipartition black-body theory. We do not even have to resort to observation in order to find this unacceptable; given the weak cosmological principle, the contracting universe is inconsistent with the second law of thermodynamics.

BONDI

Could we imagine a Wheeler-Feynman model with a universal emitter and bodies, which for lack of a better name I shall call "stars," in which helium is continuously turned into hydrogen? This is not just time reversal, because in time reversal the radiation from the universal emitter would be focused on the "stars." I do not want the radiation to be focused. I only want the "stars" to be in a heat bath. Naturally, the second law leads us to expect an inflow of heat to the "stars." Their centers will be colder than their surfaces, where the energy is consumed. It would be interesting to see if this can be worked through in detail.

MORRISON

It takes a terrible coincidence to do even this. The energy of the neutrinos must arrive at the appropriate time.

GOLD

In order for the statistical laws to take the form they have, must there be specifically a universe in which the distant background is dark and cold, and in which there are some hot spots? Would some other geometrical arrangement suffice? Would the laws hold in the case of a box with a hot side and a cold side? How specific is cosmology to the laws? I suppose that it is not very specific. It is probably necessary only that some asymmetry given by boundary conditions must be imposed on the world lines of particles in the box. The condition that the box is half hot, half cold, would suffice.

BONDI

Then Morrison's minimum cosmological requirement is really only the requirement that the universe should not be in thermal equilibrium.

MORRISON

Exactly.

LAYZER

I think we could perhaps be a little more specific in such requirements. We could require rather specific branch systems having the usual irreversibilities so that the cosmology could provide for the origin of the macroscopic systems. Obviously this is also a minimum requirement, and is not one specifically imposed by the time problem. Another requirement, I think, is some kind of statement that the universe, or its development, brings into being systems in which the microstates have a certain lack of relevance. I do not know how to formulate this. We can certainly imagine the kind of universes that X has mentioned, in which the macrostates are such that very peculiar things happen. Since these things do not in fact happen, we must either say that what we observe is a statistical freak or else that there is some deeper reason for what we observe.

BONDI

This of course is the fundamental requirement for a universe in which anybody can do science at all: that it should be possible to say something without knowing everything.

HOYLE

It seems to me that when we consider a local system, we think of the behavior of that system over a finite interval of time. Therefore we can speak of initial conditions and final conditions, but only in the sense of an arbitrary choice of the time sense. The symmetry of physical laws then means that the complete set of initial conditions and the complete set of final conditions are the same set. But if we have any rule whatever for identifying a subset of initial conditions, we should then be able to identify a subset of final conditions. These two would then not map onto each other. So it is the choice of the subset which gives the asymmetry.

ROSENFELD

But the choice of initial conditions is not a law of nature. It is the result of our position as observers.

X

But our position as observers of the world is a sort of natural law, so the choice of initial conditions also is. The laws of nature are also the results of our observations. We cannot make the universe run backwards by our own personal choice.

LAYZER

That personal choice of conditions certainly is possible when we are dealing with microscopic systems. But we do not have that latitude in dealing with the structure of the universe as a whole, because there is just one case given to us. So in the case of cosmology, the initial conditions may have the character of laws of nature.

ROSENFELD

Then one can question whether there is any meaning in talk of initial conditions.

X

I think that there is meaning in this. A physical law is ultimately a result of observation, and an hypothesis that the past was in a certain special condition is in the same category observationally. These conditions are a product of the same epistemological position as any of the other scientific laws. They are different only formally; they are not differential equations, but separate conditions. They are still products of observation; they are not *a priori* assumptions.

ROSENFELD

I quite agree. But there is a qualitative difference between the boundary conditions for a partial system and those for the universe as a whole.

This is because the term "initial conditions" always refers to an observer who is independent of what he observes.

BONDI

By "law," we usually mean differential equations which generalize many phenomena. The initial conditions then serve to reduce the generality in special cases. For the universe as a whole, the best thing that we can give is a description, not a law, because there can be only one law for the whole. So I do not like the use of the term "initial conditions" in regard to the universe as a whole. We can describe it and that is all we can do.

ROSENFELD

If this epistemological view of cosmology is taken, the distinction between initial conditions for subsystems and those for the universe tends to disappear.

LAYZER

I think that we might use different terminology for such conditions. I like to use the term "auxiliary conditions," if this is not confused with the Fermi sense. These are symmetry conditions, for instance, or any sort of condition that we use in addition to the laws to limit the freedom in the choice of solutions. In ordinary cosmology and in other problems, symmetry conditions are perfectly adequate to make the solution unique. I suspect that the auxiliary conditions that define the universe as such would have this character rather than the character of initial conditions.

GOLD

The fact that physical laws are time-symmetrical, and that the actual description of the universe is not, is in no way a bizarre or difficult point at which we should be surprised. There is nothing in this that is more surprising than the observation, for example, of a flowing river. We should be not in the least worried that the river is flowing, despite the fact that the motion of the atoms in that river is dictated by perfectly time-symmetrical laws.

X

But it is surprising and wonderful that there is asymmetry in the natural world.

BONDI

This is closely connected with the remarks by Morrison and by Layzer about branch systems. It is characteristic of the thermodynamic statement about the time's passage that time is not quantified. Entropy is said to increase, but it is not said how fast entropy increases, because we can in fact have branch systems having an arbitrary degree of perfection. We can get arbitrarily close to adiabatic conditions. Since the laws of nature therefore ought to be able to describe adiabatic conditions, they should be time-reversible and time-symmetrical.

GOLD

I would like to make a point about symmetries in general, such as that between matter and antimatter. If there is no law of physics that can distinguish matter from antimatter in an absolute fashion, then the perfect symmetry of matter and antimatter implies that we have no way of defining which of two possible kinds of universes we live in. The description of our universe should not involve the statement that there are two different possible universes and that we happen to live in one of them. As we cannot make a distinction between the two kinds of universes, we describe only what our epistemological position allows.

SCHIFF

But is it not meaningful to ask whether the universe contains both matter and antimatter?

GOLD

That question can be raised. But it is a different question. Certainly there are many problems we can raise about why we do not live in a universe different from ours. But the point is that the "mirror image" is like itself in this case, so if we understood the universe well enough, this point would never leave any arbitrariness in our description.

Now I think that the point about time asymmetry is similar. This point answers the question about the expectation of a time-asymmetrical law. However irrelevant such a law might be to actual physical processes, such a law would allow us to ask why we live in an expanding universe and not in a contracting one. If the laws are all time-symmetrical, then evidently we are obliged to explain the flow of time in terms of the processes within this universe with symmetrical laws and in terms of conditions at the end of time. In that case, there is no distinction between a contracting and an expanding universe, and we are forced to explain how, from our epistemological position, we can regard it as an expanding one.

If there is a time-asymmetrical law, then by means of it we can associate arrows or directions with the world lines of particles. These arrows are autonomous and unrelated to the cosmological motion. The arrows then can run parallel or antiparallel to the direction in which the universe moves as a whole. There would then be two different kinds of universes. But if there is no local arrow to be drawn anywhere from the laws, then these universes are the same. There are many universes still possible for consideration, of course, but not the pair with opposite motions; they are the same. Just as the matter-antimatter pair of universes cannot be distinguished, the expanding-contracting pair cannot be distinguished.

ROSENFELD

When we speak about the universe, we refer our words to certain definitions that we have agreed upon, so as to make the words communicable. One of these conventions is the specification of the sense of time—what you call the choice of an arrow. But this choice is involved not only in statements about cosmology, but in statements about all the laws of nature, and therefore it is a general physical problem whether a system obeying those particular laws will show an expansion or a contraction of the universe. The whole question may be the convention we take.

GOLD

This is a matter of convention only so long as there is no local autonomous time direction. The present physical laws possess just the degree of symmetry required to remove this "expanding-contracting" arbitrariness, an arbitrariness that would otherwise be absolutely fundamental, one which we could otherwise never remove, however well we understood physics.

MORRISON

If it were possible to make some distinction between expanding and contracting world models, this would be a philosophical distinction only. It would merely be a remarkable fact, such as the ratio of the proton mass to electron mass being 1840. I would rather see this ratio explained than have an explanation of these "time dipoles."

X

Although this discussion has been on the nature of time and particularly on reversibility or irreversibility of the universe, there are other very interesting related questions. In addition to Maxwell's equations, we have the quantum-mechanical Schrödinger equation for which every solution and its reciprocal in time are equally acceptable solutions. But with the Schrödinger equation is a lore about the interpretation of it. This interpretation seems to involve an irreversibility. For example, we calculate the probability that something *will* happen, but we do not calculate the probability that something *did* happen. In interpretation of measurement, there is a time before the measurement is made, and there is a time after the measurement is made. But after the measurement is made, the result is known, and before it is made, the result is not known. All these things are deep in the interpretational aspects of quantum mechanics.

Another question related to irreversibility has to do with the instability of the future. Tiny causes can have big effects. Given a finite error, even on the classical level, and given all information within that error, we cannot in many situations predict after a reasonable length of time what will happen. These situations show a type of instability in which novelty is produced out of infinitesimal things. That is a direction in time that is quite interesting.

Schiff

A quantum-mechanical state function which describes the universe from beginning to end must have just the same kind of reversibility properties as the equations of classical physics.

X

But how do you interpret the wave function?

Schiff

We make an observation of a piece of it.

X

That is where the irreversibility is; it is in the observation. We say that we describe the universe, but we are part of that whole wave function.

GRÜNBAUM

Measurement is analogous to the following classical example. If we have a thermodynamic system created which obeys the diffusion equation once it is closed, we can then use that equation to study the system at later times. But if we are told the system was created, and if we do not know in what condition it was created, we do not try to solve the equation backwards. Is not that analogous to the case in which a quantum-mechanical measurement is performed? We use the Schrödinger equation for subsequent times, but not for earlier times. This, of course, is an epistemological point apart from the formal dissimilarity of Schrödinger's equation and the diffusion equation.

MORRISON

How can we discuss this matter without somehow including the value of Planck's constant? I think that we seem to get away with it in talking about classical physics, but we never can do consistent classical physics. The existence of quanta, and what not, is not genuinely consistent with the assumptions of classical physics. Therefore we have somehow put in essentially quantal features of the world, even though we have not specified Planck's constant.

SCHIFF

I think that we get away with omitting Planck's constant because the essential problems that confront us are already well represented in the classical picture. We have been talking about the classical picture because it is somewhat simpler than the quantum picture and because even in this picture there are many unresolved problems. If we ever get this part completely settled so that we all agree, then we can do the same analysis with the quantum theory.

MORRISON

But if that were so, then we would be equally justified in discussing the quantum case on the grounds that the explanation in these terms would obviate the need for doing it classically.

BERGMANN

I think that the point that X raised concerning the irreversible nature of observation is distinct from Rosenfeld's previous argument. Rosenfeld addressed himself to the irreversibility represented in the macroscopic instrument which records information and which retains a record, but which did not have the record in the past, whereas X is talking more about the reduction of the wave packet. I am not concerned with the state vector of the whole universe, but with the state vector of a system outside myself that I can observe.

X

But why is it that we can predict only the probability of future events, not of past events, in quantum mechanics?

ROSENFELD

That is not true. We can just as correctly ask what is the probability that a certain state came from some other one. The result is governed by the same law.

WHEELER

I would like to make a summary of the discussion as it has impressed me. I have a general impression which surely all of us must feel in one way or another. This is a feeling of not really understanding anything. The problem is the "I" in the question, and the sharpness of this idea of "now" that goes with "I." Why is it that we have this individuality about experience? The very vividness of "now" has perhaps something of psychological character that maybe we had better avoid. We all realize from other problems in physics that it is better to attempt problems that can be solved. It is perhaps easier to give answers for some of the questions that have been brought up than it is to decide which are the right questions to be discussed. I am in no position to put forward any decisive arguments about which are the right questions, but I presume that most of us agree with Gold in the view that the initial conditions generate thermodynamics, and that if it were not for the one-sidedness in the dynamics of the universe, we as observers would not see such a one-sidedness. Rosenfeld has mentioned that the asymmetry in time may be imposed by the observer and not created by the system of which the observer forms part. It is true that the radiation reaction is quite time-symmetrical, but we can say that the past lies in the direction of time in which the boundary conditions appear simple. The striking asymmetry of the dynamics originates from this asymmetry in the boundary conditions. As regards the problem of the subjective time sense, our consensus is probably that it is produced by the one-sidedness of the dynamics of the universe. But, on the other hand, most of us would probably agree that the universe has not contained and will not contain any backward-looking observers. We do not expect to see caskets with corpses in them coming to life, nor do we expect to find bank vaults in which Morrison's gram of radium will integrate rather than disintegrate. I suppose we would be willing to call this a postulate—the "Cornell postulate."

We have agreed that the world is built according to certain rules. We cannot answer the question why the rules are just as they are, but that they come from our experience we would not deny. We are faced with the problem of man in the small and the universe in the large. The two are not completely disconnected from each other, because for life to exist with its entropy-decreasing biological mechanism, there must exist temperature difference. We could not exist for long without the sun. So from that point of view, man is the tail that is wagged by the rest of the universe. But from another point of view, the universe is the tail that is wagged by man; when the man observes, he creates a cut between himself and what he sees around him, and this cut is governed by himself. In that sense, the observer is governing his experience. It would be quite beautiful to see this point investigated in more detail.

If physics is four-dimensional, and if past, present, and future are all laid out shiningly in one vast space-time diagram, why is there any "now" in our apprehension of physics? Nothing has done more to suggest to some of us a way out of this mystery than some comments made in conversation by Hugh Everett. He compares the brain of the observer with a servomechanism, or—if I may go beyond Everett in explictness—the computer of an antiaircraft gun. The radar unit mounted on the gun carriage sights on the enemy plane. Minute by minute it feeds information about the position of that plane into the computer. From this information the computer extrapolates the future position of the plane. It then fires a shell to intercept that plane an appropriate number of minutes later. The computer thus carries within it information about a few minutes of past history—and also information about a few minutes of forthcoming history.

"It's a poor memory that only remembers backwards."—White Queen to Alice.

It would be possible for the computer to remember more, perhaps the position of the enemy plane yesterday. But that outdated information would be of no use in the present crisis. Remembering it would only impose a more complicated burden on the electronics and increase the weight to be hauled along as the gun is moved from site to site. Similarly, the computer can be forced to extrapolate the flight of the enemy plane over a much greater reach of time, even to this hour tomorrow. However, that prediction would obviously have no value whatsoever. A few minutes of the future, like a few minutes of the past, are all that the computer memory will carry. The memory span can be no wider if the antiaircraft gun is to be as light and simple as possible. Otherwise it could not stand up in the competition with rival devices. Thus the struggle for survival trims the memory down to "now." This "now" is remarkable. On it are vividly engraved not only a few minutes of the past, but also a few minutes of the future. Moreover, this "memory" (or more precisely, anticipation) of the immediate future is green, whereas the memory of yesterday has altogether withered away. So in the human species the struggle for survival—Everett's analogy would suggest—has built into our minds a type of "now" in which the old past is remembered less well than the immediate future.

Can one trace out Everett's "servomechanism explanation of *now*" in quantitative—and even quantum-mechanical—detail, on the basis of one or another simple model? Of course, devices of the feed-back type have been studied quite thoroughly, but never from exactly the point of view of interest here. We all know that when we try to describe the behavior of such devices, we use the ideas of "purpose," "planning ahead," and so on—teleological ideas, all of which form a part of our consciousness. But to fit a description of such a system, with its resistances and "dash pots," into the Hamiltonian formulation of the kind we now require is an analysis that has not yet been undertaken.

Whatever is done along these or other lines to increase our understanding of consciousness, it would appear that we still must come back to the dynamics of the universe for an explanation of the one-sidedness of time. This is the larger problem that is waiting for clarification.

The difference between past and future leads to a point that many of us have mentioned, that the universe is not a system with respect to which statistical arguments are justified. In particular, we see an enormous difference between the universe and all other mechanical systems, in respect to the distinction between equations of motion and initial conditions. Perhaps in two or three hundred years we shall have all physical laws laid down. We then will have to think about the initial conditions. First laws, then initial conditions; this is the way in which we have always approached dynamics. This method has been built into our thinking from the days when we studied freshman physics. But the idea that someday we have to face the problem of initial conditions presupposes that there *are* initial conditions for a system as all-embracing as the universe. Can it be that there is no such thing as an initial condition of the universe? Is it conceivable that there is only one possible state for the universe? We do not yet know exactly how to formulate such questions. Clearly, we can think of many different ways in which the classical machinery of the universe could be started, and many ways in which it can develop in time. It is also conceivable that each of the many possible initial states can, after sufficient time, lead to the same universe. ["Same universe" here implies the natural generalization to a dynamic continuum of an idea familiar from the mechanics of a system with a finite number of degrees of freedom: "For every $\varepsilon > 0$, however small, and for every time interval $\tau < \infty$, however large, one can always find a time $T = T_{AB}(\varepsilon, \tau)$ so great that the system coordinates, starting with initial condition A, agree at time $t + T$, within a tolerance ε, with the system coordinates at time t, starting from initial condition B, throughout the time interval $-\tau \le t \le \tau$."] Different choices of starting conditions would correspond to different points in the time development of the universe. But classical general relativity does not allow us to formulate the cosmology in this way. In every reasonable model of the closed universe, any closed spacelike hypersurface pushing its way forward in time eventually hits a singularity through which the time development cannot be continued. The classical model cannot continue to develop. Therefore we cannot check the hypothesis that the universe, started off in accordance with one initial condition, will ultimately go through every phase that would have occurred if it had started with any other initial condition.

How do we formulate these questions about initial conditions when we turn from classical general relativity, or classical geometrodynamics, to quantum geometrodynamics? Is there only one quantum state, a unique quantum state, for the idealized case of a closed matter-free universe? The answer to this question is not known.

Since these questions of principle are so difficult, perhaps it is appropriate to turn from the dynamics of the universe to a more modest problem in hopes of getting some guidance. For this reason, I think it is important to come back to the discussion of Misner and others about the fate of the contracting superdense mass. Gravitational collapse seems at first to be unrelated to the dynamics of the universe and the statistics of initial value data. However, common to the two problems— one stellar, one cosmological— are the singularities that develop in the spacelike three-geometry as it moves forward in time. According to general relativity, the nature of the singularity is much the same whether it is a star or a model universe that is collapsing. In both cases matter is calculated to arrive in a finite proper time at a condition of infinite density. In both cases the sharpness of curvature of spacelike hypersurfaces goes to infinity outside matter as well as inside. Light signals may get outside the crunching matter to carry news of the impending catastrophe. Yet in both cases these light rays travel in a geometry that is itself collapsing. Thus the signals themselves are overtaken by catastrophe.

No one of us believes that a reasonable physical quantity—like density of matter or curvature of space—really goes to infinity. Instead, all our experience indicates that a prediction of "infinity" is to be understood as a prediction that new and perhaps unexpected physical phenomena have yet to be taken into account.

As a reminder that an "infinity" warns of new physics around the corner, no one can forget the infinity associated with the Rutherford atom of 1911. The electron spirals into the Coulomb center of attraction, arriving in a finite time—according to classical theory—at a condition of infinite kinetic energy. This prediction stood in the most direct conflict with the observed stability of atoms. Moreover, no modification in the law of radiation, nor any change in the law of attraction between electron and nucleus, offered an acceptable way out of the difficulty. Instead, a new physical feature had to be recognized as dominating the situation—the quantum of action. Not that the workers of Rutherford's day readily agreed that the quantum principle was either necessary or sufficient to resolve the paradox of atomic stability! It seemed so much easier to try one or another change in the laws of radiation or in the law of attraction between electron and nucleus. Today, confronted with the paradox of gravitational collapse, many would likewise seek an escape by postulating high elasticity for highly compressed matter. However, we have all been through this discussion. We know that the speed of sound cannot exceed the speed of light if causality is to be upheld. Matter can put up only a strictly limited resistance against collapse. No way has ever been found to escape the inevitability of the collapse of a supercritical mass without giving up one or another strongly held principle.

Accept that collapse occurs (classical geometrodynamics)—and accept also that a singularity ultimately develops in the geometry (classical geometrodynamics followed to the limit). This is Misner's proposal. The first part of it we can agree to. I do not see how we can accept the second part. If we are to admit for one place a singularity in the solutions of the equations of relativity, we can admit a singularity somewhere else. If we admit them at several places, we can also think of a continuous distribution of singularities. But a continuous distribution of singularities of arbitrary strength is only another way of speaking of an arbitrary source. And with an arbitrary source standing on the right-hand side of the field equations, these equations no longer mean anything. It would appear, then, that we must exclude singularities. Yet the classical treatment of the collapse of a star or of the collapse of a model universe always leads to singularity. It is difficult to name any issue which is more likely to force us into new thinking than the paradox of gravitational collapse. It has sometimes been asked, What happens when an irresistible force meets an immovable object? The famous answer has always been: It goes through without leaving a hole behind it. No similar joke saves us from worrying about the paradox of gravitational collapse. There is no trivial answer to today's question, "What happens next?," when a finite amount of matter is compressed into an indefinitely small proper volume. Are we right to keep trying to answer this question? Is it not time to question the question?

Does the phrase "what happens next" really have meaning? Implicit in the concept of "next" is the idea that all events are imbedded in a space-time manifold with a definite causal relationship one to another. On this classical view it makes sense to ask "what happens next" after a given event. It also makes sense to speak of a spacelike slice, or three-geometry, $^{(3)}\mathcal{G}$, cutting through this four-geometry. A succession of such slices can be established. Each supplies a record of "what happens next" after the spacelike slice before it. The entire collection of three-geometries can even be conceived as "nesting together" to make up the four-geometry. In geometrodynamics, space-time may be conceived to be built up in this way out of spacelike slices much as in particle dynamics a world line may be considered to be built up out of successive space-time points. The laws of particle dynamics tell which space-time points will be used and which will be discarded in the construction of the world line. Einstein's field equations similarly tell which three-geometries will be used and which will be discarded in the construction of the space-time manifold.

All this changes when we turn from classical geometrodynamics to quantum general relativity. The totality of all conceivable spacelike three-geometries no longer falls apart into two sharply distinct classes: a small class that gets used in the construction of a space-time manifold, and a much larger class that does not. Instead, there is a probability amplitude for this, that, and the other three-geometry—a complex number which depends upon the three-geometry, and upon the three-geometry alone, and which is governed in its dependence upon this three-geometry by a Schrödinger equation. No longer can the three-geometries that occur with appreciable probability amplitude be nested together into a four-geometry. No longer is it even justified to use the term "the space-time manifold."

We have been brought up to think of all physics as taking place within a four-dimensional manifold, and of every event as having a well-defined location with respect to every other event within this manifold. We have always tacitly assumed everything we have done, or are now doing, or ever will do, to have it own place within this all embracing Einsteinian catalog of history—past, present, and future. In contrast, quantum geometrodynamics tells us that there is no such four-geometry. There is no unambiguous way to conclude that such and such three-geometry is encountered before (or after) such and such another three-geometry. The concept of time as we normally use it is completely out of place in the context of quantum geometrodyanmics. The ideas of "before" and "after" lose all meaning.

Only in the limit, where the spread of a wave packet is small compared to the scale of the effects under study, is there a correspondence between the predictions of quantum and classical geometrodynamics. Only in this limit does there exist an approximate time ordering of three-geometries into a single all-embracing four-geometry. Only in this limit does the idea of "before" and "after" make sense. However, as high densities and curvatures are approached in the final stages of gravitational collapse, and as the relevant physical dimensions approach the scale of the Planck length, $(\hbar G/c^3)$, it is no longer possible to describe what happens in the language of wave packets. One has instead to use the language of quantum theory. One is tempted to speak of probability amplitudes for this, that, and the other "outcome." But even the familiar applications of quantum electrodynamics do not supply sufficient background for the new concepts that are forced on one by quantum geometrodynamics. The very word "outcome" carries overtones of the idea of "after the collapse." But the quantum context is one where precisely the concept of "before and after" loses its significance. In brief, we face quite new and unexpected aspects of the concept of time when we deal with the final stages of gravitational collapse within the framework of quantum geometrodynamics.

ROSENFELD

There is a noticeable tendency on the part of some people to consider quantization as a sort of machine, or process, which is operated for any kind of system in the hope of finding significant results. But it is not so easy. There is no clear-cut answer to the question about whether it is meaningful to quantize the gravitational field, or whether gravitational quanta exist. I should perhaps start by pointing out that the answer to this is not even clear-cut in radiation theory. Indeed, the existence of light quanta is a fact of experience, and if we had not known this fact, we could not have deduced it in any way from the development of mechanics, and not even from the application of it. We can, of course, formally apply quantization to the oscillators by which we describe the radiation field, but we cannot be sure beforehand whether this corresponds to reality. The situation is still more difficult in the case of the gravitational field, because we have no experimental evidence that there are gravitational quanta. Moreover, there seem to be certain difficulties as regards the possibility of defining a concentration of energy of the order $\hbar c/\lambda$ within a domain of linear dimensions λ, when the wavelength λ is of the order of atomic lengths. This is because in the theory of gravitation there are critical quantities having the dimensions of mass and length, which seem to impose stricter limitations on such concentrations of energy. This argument is, however, not cogent, but only an indication of possible difficulties. It is clear that if experimental evidence showed that gravitation quanta exist, means would be found to overcome such difficulties.

People have raised the question whether it is possible to have peaceful coexistence between the quantized theory of radiation and matter on the one hand, and unquantized gravitational theory on the other. I do not think that there is any logical difficulty here, because after all this amounts to deciding with the classical equations of gravitation how we are to define the $T_{\mu\nu}$, the tensor representing the influence of other fields in interaction with the gravitational field. This is a matter which has to be decided by experience; it cannot be decided by any purely logical reasoning. This $T_{\mu\nu}$ could not be the operator expressed in terms of quantized fields, of course, but it could very well be the expectation value of such a tensor, for the states considered.

GOLD

I see a great problem in this. If gravitational theory is not quantized, then surely we could infringe the uncertainty principle with information gathered from gravitational waves and such. The quantum theory is only logically consistent provided that all its own rules are satisfied whatever influences are involved. There might be some degree of quantization required.

ROSENFELD

I do not think this implies a degree of quantization, but it implies a limitation of the validity of the quantized equations, surely. All our experience of the gravitational field is on the cosmical scale, and we do not know how gravitation appears on the atomic scale. Certain people have insisted that we are forced on logical grounds to quantize gravitation, because of the existence of other quantized fields. I do not see any such compulsion; I only insist that the question is absolutely open.

BERGMANN

On the formal level I have no argument against this; I agree. As for the specific model of quantized interaction that was suggested by Møller, the one in which the expectation value of mass density appears as the source of gravity, I find this model not particularly appealing because the expectation value changes when a quantum-mechanical observation is performed and one state is substituted for another state of the quantum system. As a result, the expectation values change in a manner not governed by any dynamical principle.

As far as I can see, we have two possibilities. One is, as you suggest, that the gravitational field equations may have serious limitations, and I am convinced that this is true in any event. I do not believe in the eternal truth of any physical theory. The other possibility is that there are in truth hidden parameters. In this case, it would be legitimate to describe gravitation as a classical field, but because we observe the gravitational field by means of real test particles, which themselves are subject to uncertainty relations, we are as a matter of principle incapable of measuring all these perfectly well-defined phenomena. On the one hand, we have the theory of gravitation; on the other, quantum theory. They are both reasonably well established. If they can be united, fine. But if this program is unsuccessful, then we can learn something from the failure. I have never taken a view different from this one.

ROSENFELD

My motivation in 1930 for quantizing gravitation was only to explore the formal possibilities of this new method, and the specific point then was to understand the origin of the difficulties of convergence in quantum electrodynamics. We wanted to know whether such difficulties would be present also for other sources than point charges, and the case of the gravitation field of a photon provided such an example. In any case, we should not introduce any exclusion principles into physics other than that sanctified by the name of Pauli, or, at any rate, principles of empirical origin. This should not prevent people from exploring possibilities, even though there is not really a logical necessity for quantization.

MISNER

But this depends on what we mean by "quantizing." If we define the word "quantizing" to mean only "modifying the existing classical equations in view of the quantum aspects of other parts of physics," then I think we can say things must be quantized.

ROSENFELD

An argument was put forward by Henley and Thirring that the analysis of the field measurements showed that the electromagnetic field must be quantized. What has been proved, however, is the reciprocal statement, since in the argument the limitations depending upon h have been deduced from the assumed decomposition of the electromagnetic field into photons. But if that is not done, and the radiative interactions are described classically, then we find that all measurements are perfectly compatible without observable limitation.

GOLD

This brings the meeting to a close. I want to thank everyone present for having been so patient, so persevering, and so instructive in wrestling with this subject. We cannot claim to have solved the main problems. I believe, however, that we have all obtained a better view of the problem, and that we have all got a better understanding of the divergent views that exist. It may be that no very profound improvement in our understanding of time will ever take place; but it could also be that some new physical theory will be devised one day that depends on, or defines, a different concept for time. How philosophical concepts can be changed as a result of new physical theories was best demonstrated by relativity theory giving a new meaning to the relationship between space and time. I personally think that our present understanding is inadequate and is perhaps holding us back from a better description of nature, one that is less dependent on our subjective notions. Many thanks for your participation.

Notes and References

Introduction (T. GOLD)

References

T. Gold, "The Arrow of Time," in *Onzième Conseil de Physique Solvay: "La Structure et l'Evolution de l'Univers"* (Brussels: R. Stoops, 1958), pp. 81–95; also in *Recent Developments in General Relativity*, (Oxford, New York: Pergamon, 1962), pp. 225–234.

T. Gold, "The Arrow of Time" (21st Richtmyer Memorial Lecture, Amer. Phys. Soc. Meeting, New York, Jan., 1962), *Am. J. Phys.*, **30** (1962), 403.

I. Absorber Theory of Radiation (J. HOGARTH)

Note

1. See *Proc. R. Soc., Ser. A*, **267** (1962), 365.

II. Time-Symmetrical Electrodynamics and Cosmology (F. HOYLE AND J. V. NARLIKAR)

Note

1. See *Proc. R. Soc., Ser. A.*, **270** (1962), 334.

III. Cosmological Boundary Conditions for Zero Rest-Mass Fields (R. PENROSE)

References

W. Rindler, *Mon. Not. R. Astr. Soc.*, **116** (1956), 662.

R. Penrose, "Conformal Treatment of Infinity," in *Relativity, Groups and Topology: The 1963 Les Houches Lectures*, ed. C. DeWitt and B. DeWitt, (New York: Gordon and Breach, 1964), pp. 565–584.

R. Penrose, *Proc. R. Soc., Ser. A*, **284** (1965), 159.

IV. Retarded Potentials and the Expansion of the Universe (D. W. SCIAMA)

Note

1. See *Proc. R. Soc., Ser. A.*, **273** (1963), 484.

VI. Infinite Red-Shifts in General Relativity (C. MISNER)

Notes

1. J. R. Oppenheimer and H. Snyder, *Phys. Rev.*, **56** (1939), 455.
2. Unpublished B.S. thesis, Princeton University, Mathematics Department, 1961.
3. S. Chandrasekhar, *Mon. Not. R. Astr. Soc.*, **91** (1931), 456, and **95** (1935), 207,

reviewed in *An Introduction to the Study of Stellar Structure* (Chicago: University of Chicago Press, 1939).

4. J. R. Oppenheimer and G. M. Volkoff, *Phys. Rev.*, **55** (1939), 374; see also L. D. Landau and E. M. Lifshitz, *Statistical Physics* (Reading, Mass.: Addison-Wesley, 1958), 108.

5. B. K. Harrison, M. Wakano, and J. A. Wheeler in *Onzième Conseil de Physique Solvay: "La Structure et l'Evolution de l'Univers"* (Brussels: R. Stoops, 1958), and subsequently ch. 10 in B. K. Harrison, K. S. Thorne, M. Wakano, and J. A. Wheeler, *Gravitation Theory and Gravitational Collapse* (Chicago: University of Chicago Press, 1965).

6. V. A. Ambartsumyan and G. S. Saakyan, *Soviet Astron. AJ*, **4** (1960), 187.

7. K. Schwarzschild, *Berl. Ber.* (1916), 424.

8. J. A. Wheeler, "Geometrodynamics and the Issue of the Final State," in *Relativity, Groups and Topology: The 1963 Les Houches Lectures* (New York: Gordon and Breach, 1964), pp. 317–520.

9. In a private communication.

10. C. Møller, *The Theory of Relativity* (Oxford: Clarendon, 1952), p. 124.

11. M. D. Kruskal, *Phys. Rev.*, **119** (1960), 1743; see also R. W. Fuller and J. A. Wheeler, *Phys. Rev.*, **128** (1962), 919.

VIII. The Strong Cosmological Principle, Indeterminacy, and the Direction of Time (D. LAYZER)

References

"A Preface to Cosmogony: I. The Energy Equation and the Virial Theorem for Cosmic Distributions," *Ap. J.*, **138** (July, 1963), 174.

"The Formation of Stars and Galaxies: Unified Hypotheses," *Annual Reviews of Astronomy and Astrophysics*, **2** (1964).

"A Unified Approach to Cosmology," paper presented in the Summer Seminar on Relativity Theory and Astrophysics, sponsored by the American Mathematical Society, 1965.

IX. The Instability of the Future (P. MORRISON)

Note

1. A more rigorous treatment separate from the discussions presented here appears in brief in *Preludes in Theoretical Physics*, ed. A. de-Shalit *et al.* (Amsterdam: North-Holland, 1966), p. 347.

X. The Anisotropy of Time (A. GRÜNBAUM)

Notes

1. This is an amended version of the paper presented at this meeting. The original version appeared in *Monist*, **48** (1964), 219.

2. H. Weyl, *Philosophy of Mathematics and Natural Science* (Princeton: Princeton University Press, 1949), p. 116. For a critique of basic misunderstandings and irrelevant criticisms of Weyl's statement by Max Black and Milič Čapek, see A. Grünbaum, *Philosophical Problems of Space and Time* (New York: Knopf, 1963), ch. 10. Hereinafter

this work will be cited as *PPST*. A *detailed* defense of the thesis that coming into being is anthropocentric (mind-dependent) is given in A. Grünbaum, "The Status of Temporal Becoming," *Annals of the New York Academy of Sciences* **138** (1967), 374–395, and in A. Grünbaum, *Modern Science and Zeno's Paradoxes* (Middletown: Wesleyan University Press, 1967), ch. 1.

3. H. Reichenbach, *The Philosophy of Space and Time* (New York: Dover, 1958), pp. 138–139.

4. Cf. H. Reichenbach, "Les Fondements Logiques de la Mécanique des Quanta," *Annales de l'Institut Poincaré*, **13** (1953), 154–157.

5. H. Bondi, "Relativity and Indeterminacy," *Nature*, **169** (1952), 660.

6. I am indebted to Professor Wilfrid Sellars for having made clarifying remarks to me in 1956 which relate to this point: see his "Time and the World Order," in *Scientific Explanation, Space and Time*, ed. H. Feigl and G. Maxwell, (Minneapolis: University of Minnesota Press, 1962), for a very illuminating treatment of issues related to the contents of §1 and §2 of this paper.

7. P. W. Bridgman, *Reflections of a Physicist* (New York: Philosophical Library, 1950), pp. 163 and 165.

8. I am indebted to my colleague Professor A. Janis for pointing out to me (by reference to the example of having dreamt) that condition (1) is only a sufficient and not also a necessary condition for the obtaining of the relation of being psychologically later.

9. Cf. A. S. Eddington, *The Nature of the Physical World* (New York: Macmillan, 1928), pp. 68–69 and ch. 5.

10. O. Penrose and I. C. Percival, "The Direction of Time," *Proc. Phys. Soc.*, **79** (1962), 606.

11. H. Reichenbach, *The Direction of Time* (Berkeley: University of California Press, 1956).

12. *Ibid.*, p. 118.

13. Cf. R. C. Tolman, *The Principles of Statistical Mechanics* (Oxford: Oxford University Press, 1938), p. 149.

14. Cf. R. Fürth, "Prinzipien der Statistik," *Handbuch der Physik*, **4** (1929), 270 and 192–193.

15. *Ibid.*, p. 270.

16. Although the decisive asymmetry just noted was admitted by H. Mehlberg ("Physical Laws and Time's Arrow," in *Current Issues in the Philosophy of Science*, ed. H. Feigl and G. Maxwell [New York: Holt, Rinehart and Winston, 1961], p. 129), he dismisses it as expressing "merely the factual difference between the two relevant values of probability." But an asymmetry is no less an asymmetry for depending on *de facto*, contingent boundary conditions rather than being assured by a *law* alone. Since our verification of laws generally has the same partial and indirect character as that of our confirmation of the existence of complicated *de facto* boundary conditions, the assertion of an asymmetry depending on *de facto* conditions is generally no less reliable than one wholly grounded on a law. Hence, when Mehlberg (*ibid.*, p. 117, n. 30) urges against Schrödinger's claim of entropic asymmetry that, for every pair of branch-systems which change their entropy in one direction, "there is nothing to prevent" another pair of closed subsystems from changing their entropy in the opposite direction, the reply is: Mehlberg's criticism can be upheld only by gratuitously neglecting the statistical asymmetry admitted but then dismissed by him as "merely" factual. For it is the existence of the specified boundary conditions which statistically prevents the existence of entropic time symmetry in this context. The reader is referred to my book *PPST*, ch. 8, for a critique of Mehlberg's further contention that Carathéodory's axiomatic account of the

second law of thermodynamics "has also stripped the second phenomenological principle of thermodynamics of its irreversible and anisotropic implications."

17. Cf. K. R. Popper, *Nature*, **181** (1958), 402. For my rebuttal of a similar objection by Carnap, see A. Grünbaum, *PPST*, pp. 278–280.

18. Cf. Penrose and Percival, *op. cit.*, §9, p. 614.

19. H. Reichenbach, *The Direction of Time*, p. 136.

20. *Ibid.*, pp. 132–133.   21. *Ibid.*, p. 126.

22. Cf. K. P. Stanyukovič, "On the Increase of Entropy in an Infinite Universe," *Doklady, Akademiia Nauk SSSR*, N.S., **69** (1949), 793, in Russian, as summarized by L. Tisza in *Math. Rev.*, **12** (1951), 787.

23. For additional doubts concerning the cosmological relevance of the entropy concept. cf. L. Landau and E. Lifshitz, *Statistical Physics* (2nd ed.; New York, Addison-Wesley, 1958), pp. 22–27.

24. Cf. A. Grünbaum, *PPST*, ch. 9.

25. This is *not* to say that there are not *other* initial conditions under which at least a finite portion of the system's past can be inferred. For a discussion of this case, see J. C. Maxwell, *Theory of Heat* (6th ed.; New York: Longmans, Green, 1880), and F. John, "Numerical Solution of the Equation of Heat Conduction for Preceding Times," *Annali di Matematica Pura ed Applicata*, **40** (1955), 129. For a different account of the connection between irretrodictability and irreversibility, see S. Watanabe, "Time and the Probabilistic View of the World," in J. T. Fraser, ed., *The Voices of Time* (New York: George Braziller, 1966), pp. 543 ff.

26. K. R. Popper, in *Nature*, **177** (1956), 538; **178** (1956), 382; **179** (1957), 1297; **181** (1958), 402. These four publications will be cited hereinafter as "I," "II," "III," and "IV," respectively.

27. E. L. Hill and A. Grünbaum, "Irreversible Processes in Physical Theory," *Nature*, **179** (1957), 1296.

28. Penrose and Percival, *op. cit.*, p. 611.

29. O. Costa de Beauregard, "L'Irréversibilité Quantique, Phenomène Macroscopique," *Louis de Broglie, Physicien et Penseur* (Paris: Albin Michel, 1953). For Costa de Beauregard's own evaluation of Popper's ideas, see the former's "Irreversibility Problems," *Proceedings of the 1964 International Congress for Logic, Methodology and Philosophy of Science* (Amsterdam: North-Holland, 1965), p. 319. See also that author's recent book *Le Second Principe de la Science du Temps* (Paris: Editions du Seuil, 1963).

30. Hill and Grünbaum, *op. cit.*

31. Cf. G. J. Whitrow, *The Natural Philosophy of Time* (London: Thomas Nelson and Sons, 1961), pp. 8–10 and 269; also E. Zilsel, "Über die Asymmetrie der Kausalität und die Einsinnigkeit der Zeit," *Naturwissenschaften*, **15** (1927), 283.

32. I must refer to my book *PPST* for my reply to Popper and to Mehlberg, as well as for a rebuttal to H. Mehlberg's denial of the anisotropy of time.

33. T. Gold, "The Arrow of Time," in *Onzième Conseil de Physique Solvay: "La Structure et l'Evolution de l'Univers"* (Brussels: R. Stoops, 1958), pp. 86–87. Cf. also Gold's different paper of the same title, published in *Am. J. Phys.*, **30** (1962), 403.

34. Presumably Gold is referring here to models of spatially closed or finite universes.

35. Gold, "The Arrow of Time," *Am. J. Phys.*, pp. 404–405.

XII. Time and Physical Language (D. L. Schumacher)

Notes

1. This article is a revision of the paper presented at this meeting. The work was supported by AFOSR contract 49(638)-1527.

2. N. Bohr, paper III in *Atomic Theory and the Description of Nature* (Cambridge: Cambridge University Press, 1961).

3. N. Bohr, "Unity of Knowledge," in *Atomic Physics and Human Knowledge* (New York: Wiley and Sons, 1958).

4. N. Bohr, "Atoms and Human Knowledge," in *Atomic Physics and Human Knowledge.*

5. N. Bohr, "Physical Science and the Problem of Life," in *Atomic Physics and Human Knowledge.*

6. N. Bohr, "Discussion with Einstein," in *Atomic Physics and Human Knowledge.*

7. Von Neumann, *Mathematical Foundations of Quantum Mechanics* (Princeton: Princeton University Press, 1955).

8. Schrödinger, "On the Peculiarity of the Scientific World-View," in *What is Life?* (New York: Doubleday, 1956).

9. Schrödinger, *Mind and Matter* (Cambridge: Cambridge University Press, 1959).

10. Schrödinger, "The Spirit of Science," in *What is Life?*

11. There is a useful review of recent pertinent work on perception in the Appendix, "Physics and Perception," in *The Special Theory of Relativity* by D. Bohm (New York: Benjamin, 1965). It may be helpful to examine some of the general remarks and conclusions made there. The notion of a separation of subject and object is discussed in other terms, and while it is rightly emphasized in the context that this notion is itself learned together with the terms of a physical description which is not of an absolute character, the general conclusions given there tend to attribute absolute significance to the separation of subject and object. In particular, the reliance on the notions of a so-called "inner show," and of the entity to which it refers, essentially prejudges the separation of subject and object to be an absolute. (Cf. especially *ibid.*, p. 204, par. 1, and pp. 216–217.) In this connection, it is instructive to appreciate that Bohr, in writing on these questions, rarely used terms of this kind; if they were used, they were clearly not intended to bear the full weight of the arguments. Even though Bohr apparently tended to give absolute significance to the separation of subject and object, he did not do so by means of particular terms which might be mistaken to establish the absoluteness of this notion.

12. N. Wiener, *Cybernetics* (New York: Wiley and Sons, 1948).

13. In connection with this, it is helpful to contrast different views on the logical character of the time problem. To be specific, let us contrast the attitudes of Morrison, Bergmann (p. 189), and the present paper. It is important to realize that some of the relevant terms are used differently by different persons, so a sort of interlingual dictionary is required:

C.G. = coarse-graining or "curtailing of information";
E.P.A. = explicit probabilistic assumption or "prejudgment."

P. M.	P. B.	D. S.
"Statistics" = C.G. "irreversibility" = instability	"statistics" = C.G. "irreversibility" = C.G. + E.P.A.	"statistics" = C.G. + E.P.A. "irreversibility" = statistics (S)
	Logical Summary	
C.G. ⇒ "irreversibility (M)"	C.G. ≠ "irreversibility"	(1) C.G. ≠ E.P.A. (2) Point (1) allows associating statistical irreversibility with the idea of time in the synthetical aspect of language.

14. S. Körner, ed., *Observation and Interpretation* (London: Butterworths and Co., 1957).

15. Cf. Schrödinger, *Nature*, **153** (1944), 704.